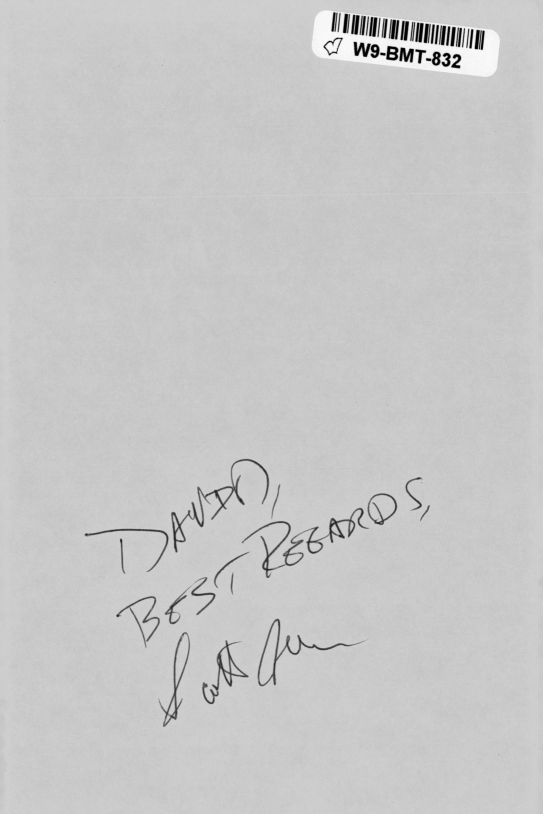

DAVID,
BEST REGARDS,

Relationship
MATTERS

THE *FOUNDATION* OF
MEDICAL CARE IS *FRACTURING*

DR. SCOTT JENSEN

SJ

CatalystMedicalClinic.com

The medical fable, "Mrs. Bear's Final Illness," was used by permission of Richard J. Feinstein, M.D., from his book, *Ethical Conflicts in Daily Medical Practice*, Infinity Publishing, 1094 New DeHaven Street, Suite 100, West Conshohochen, PA 19428-2713.

Literary development and design: Koechel Peterson & Associates, Inc., Mpls., MN.

Books may be ordered by calling Catalyst Medical Clinic, PA at 952-955-1963

ISBN 978-0-9965244-0-7

Printed in the United States of America

WITH THANKSGIVING AND LOVE,

this book is dedicated to

my incredible wife, Mary,

and our amazing children, Cristy, Matt, and Jackie.

I was born and raised in the quiet little town of Sleepy Eye in the southern plains of Minnesota. It was a community in which safety was never an issue, and the entire village participated in raising its children. I was the middle child of five. Mom was my best friend, and Dad was my hero. Tragically, both my parents died young . . . too young.

My career search took place on the heels of Mom's passing, and it wasn't a straight path. It included a year in dental school followed by a year in the seminary. Then a brief detour into the universe of law found me taking exams and preparing for law school, but finally I decided on medical school. It was in the hallowed corridors of hospitals that I fell in love with taking care of people, and this love affair has endured for nearly forty years. Focusing on the physical, emotional, and spiritual aspects of my patients' well-being continues to intrigue me—they bless me daily.

Hobbies provide a necessary diversion from illness and suffering, and golfing, flying, skiing, and bowling provide me with rejuvenation and thankfulness for an abundant life.

Presently I live and practice medicine in the western suburbs of Minneapolis, and I thank God for my lovely wife, Mary, a practicing veterinarian, and my three children: Cristy, Matt, and Jackie. The blessings Mary and I received from raising and loving our three children go beyond the magic of mere words.

My years of "doctoring" have granted me immense confidence that departing this planet will lead to the ultimate blessing when I step through the door leading to God's side of eternity. My conviction that we never stand alone is reflected in words from Habakkuk 3:2, *Lord, I have heard of your fame; I stand in awe of your deeds, Lord. Repeat them in our day, in our time make them known.* I believe God is repeating His awesome deeds in our day, but too often we are blinded by a pride—spawned by our own intellect—that obscures our vision and prevents us from fully realizing the joys and gifts our Creator has bestowed upon us.

My prayer is that I live life better today than I did yesterday, and tomorrow I will do better still.

ACKNOWLEDGMENTS

My first note of thanks must be to the people whose stories comprise this book, for they have allowed me into their sacrosanct and special lives. I also recognize with gratitude each of the patients I serve on a regular basis; they humble me with their grace and wisdom, and they renew me.

As my initial guide, Shannon Pennefeather assisted me with her invaluable editing skills and a balance of gracious words, critical comments, and the reminder to avoid "getting on a soapbox."

Several people helped shape the stories and pinpoint the lessons within this manuscript by injecting ideas, passion, sensitivity, timing, and humor. They motivated me to write creatively in order to validate the time and insight they gave to this project, and I did not want to disappoint them. Thanks to these wonderful folks: Ken and Marlys Jenson for topline editing; Nancy and Paul Tollefsrud for ongoing encouragement and the occasional admonition to "keep it short and don't be boring"; Pastor Brian Fragodt for insight into what I was trying to say and suggestions that eased me past temporary barriers; Rory Eoin O'Sullivan for smoothing out the dialogue and holding off any punch line until the last possible moment; Shari Wagner for pointing out moments of poignancy that would make people want to read my stories; Janet Forstrom for her never-ending delight in brainstorming; and Pastor Joel Johnson for his motivating declaration that I was pioneering a path he might choose to follow.

David Koechel, John Peterson, Lance Wubbels, and David Abeler are the experts who shepherded my labor of love through its final stages of development, and I am immensely grateful for their efforts.

Tom and Dianne Perbix have blessed my family with love and support for years. Without them, Catalyst Medical Clinic would not be; without them, this book would not have been written; without them, my career in private practice would have vanished a long time ago. You're the best, Tom and Dianne.

My wife, Mary, has been the wind beneath my wings for forty years. As Ruth pledged to Naomi in the Old Testament, "Where you go I will go, and where you stay I will stay," Mary has done the same for me, supporting me in all my ventures. She is my best friend and my love, and her impact on this book is indelibly etched in some way or another on each and every page. Words fall short, Mary.

CONTENTS

Dr. Scott Jensen's *Relationship Matters* is captivating from the start. The compelling narratives reveal his commitment for putting people first—they matter. I'm not surprised. He's my doc and has cared for me, my wife, Keri, and our four adult children for years. We have benefited firsthand from his extraordinary knowledge and his compassionate care that integrates best practices with personal understanding. We trust him.

These real-life stories will seize and stretch your mind with nuggets of profound wisdom for living well. They will enlarge your heart with their gravitational pull that draws you right next to Scott's side in the chaotic rush of the ER, on the turbulent floor of a plane 37,000 feet in the air, in the calm living room of the infirmed, and even in his Catalyst Medical Clinic for normal checkups.

Scott doesn't tiptoe around the need to speak straightforward truth in love, even when the diagnosis is less than desired. His views on today's changing health care system expose the challenges facing us as a nation and will help you to pause, take a deep breath, and examine your own voice of advocacy. Best of all, you will celebrate the beauty of life and honor.

DR. JOEL K. JOHNSON
Founding Pastor, Westwood Community Church
Adjunct Professor, Bethel University

T HREE DECADES AGO, a young doctor—equipped with book learning and the confidence of youth— departed the nurturing cocoon of his training program ready to reach out and heal the sick and fix the wounded. He may have anticipated wonders and oddities in the care of his fellow man, but the biggest revelation he came across was a lesson about giving and receiving. His immediate expectation, devoid of experience, was that of transactional encounters with patients: medical care in exchange for some type of payment. He was surprised to learn that mere compensation for services rendered seemed paltry compared to the mutual appreciation and respect that could be generated between patient and doctor. He came to understand that meaningful relationships with patients energized and sustained his commitment to his profession and made him strive to be the best doctor he could be.

That young man was me. I was thankful for that discovery then, and thirty years later I am still in awe of the gifts derived from serving patients, especially the mutual appreciation and respect that foster the development of patient trust and physician advocacy—vital cornerstones for healing and renewal.

ɪɕ ɪɕ ɪɕ

REGRETTABLY, something changed: a multitude of circumstances and so-called advancements brought about dehumanization in the way doctors serve patients, and the importance of the patient-doctor relationship diminished. The lifeblood of medicine—a bond built on trust and advocacy between the receiver and provider of care—is in jeopardy, and it's time to confront the fracturing relationship before it's too late.

Let me begin by going back to my story.

◌ ◌ ◌

THE 1960S WERE HISTORY, and our country was on the move, searching for answers. A farewell to Vietnam, Nixon, Watergate, and Woodstock was followed by a sobering how-do-you-do with gas rationing, double-digit inflation, and a populace uncertain about the future.

And me? I also was on the move, uncertain about the future, and searching for my place in the world. Saying farewell to the draft, dental school, and the seminary, I scrutinized my options, wondering where I might best fit, and during this time of exploration, I examined the possibility of a career as a physician. This consideration grew and soon became a passion, challenging me to go the distance.

And so I did. I studied and took exams. I applied and was accepted to medical school. I dissected cadavers, learned chemical equations, and memorized physical laws. I finished medical school and completed a three-year residency in family practice. I was enthused. I had found my career.

But I also found something else. From my very first clerkships, I came to realize how much I enjoyed the opportunity to connect with my patients. Rigorous sixteen-hour shifts filled with drawing blood, holding surgical clamps, and performing physical exams were far more tolerable if at the end of the day I judged that my patients and I had developed a working bond built on their trust and my advocacy of their needs. For me this was the most desirable outcome in serving the ill and the injured, for then I was uplifted. Doctoring seemed a calling—not a job—and I learned how special it was to be invited into patients' sacrosanct lives. My search for a place in the world was over.

But, as I indicated earlier, the way we care for patients changed— dramatically. Today a long-standing pillar of medical care—the relationship between patient and healer—is under siege, and never-ending maneuverings in the health care industry routinely sabotage this connection by minimizing its value. This bond has been tarnished by the power of the dollar, the lure of marketing, the curse of unrealistic expectations, and a thirst for control. These intrusions have transformed the art of caring into a sad state of affairs that threatens to destroy the value of the traditional patient-doctor relationship.

The provision and reception of health care services is "a business" for the industry's mega stakeholders—insurance companies, government agencies, hospital/clinic consortiums, and public/corporate cartels— and these entities are in the process of reshaping the field of medicine with only casual regard for the insights of patients and physicians. Their focus is on profit, market share, and control, and they pay scant attention to the tender aspects of end-of-life care or patient fears regarding risky litigation-driven interventions.

Patients and doctors should not be content to view this changing landscape of medical care from the outside looking in. The manner in which the sick, wounded, and dying are being cared for has changed immensely, and plans for even more dramatic changes are already being discussed in boardrooms and the halls of government institutions. These are frightening times for patients and doctors alike, and apathy will have a cost.

CONSIDER SOME PATIENT ISSUES:

Patients want to be more than a mere number; they want to confer with a doctor directly without an intervening computer screen; they want to speak with a real person about an abnormal lab test; they are not enamored with electronic voices incapable of individualized responses; they are fearful that personal information will end up on Facebook due to Internet hacking.

Is it reasonable to expect patients to accept the role of dutiful subjects for whom pills are prescribed, in whom catheters are inserted, and on whom surgeries are conducted? Is it agreed that patients should have the right to consent to a blood test, decline a Lipitor prescription, decline a flu shot, and choose their doctor? Are patients being encouraged— or even allowed—to manage their own health care needs, or has Big Brother assumed a role not requested of him?

CONSIDER SOME PHYSICIAN ISSUES:

Is it realistic to think physicians can maintain career satisfaction and commitment in the challenging arena of sickness and death without the renewing energy that comes from meaningful patient relationships? Can physicians recapture the spirit of seeing patients as a treasure and sense the privilege of advocating for those they serve? Is physician burnout an inevitable outcome as the mega stakeholders demand control, oversight, electronic medical records, quotas, penalties, and prior authorizations?

This book is first and foremost about patients: their wisdom, their preciousness, and their ability to reenergize those who serve them. It is also about doctors: their challenges, their fears, and their foibles as they struggle with a virtual epidemic of disillusionment. Last but not least, it examines the matter of relationships, focusing on bonds between patients and doctors, but it also draws attention to impaired connections between patients and insurance companies, doctors and hospitals, and doctors and doctors. This list of casualties grows as the heart of medicine is infiltrated by an inscrutable contagion determined to change forever the manner in which caregivers minister to the sick, wounded, and dying.

Relationship Matters: The Foundation of Medical Care Is Fracturing challenges the reader to consider the ramifications of this new era of patient-doctor relationships and assess the importance of reclaiming these time-honored bonds. The survival of patient-driven, physician-guided health care is at stake. The assertion from Ayn Rand, "You can avoid reality, but you cannot avoid the consequences of avoiding reality," is hauntingly applicable.

Each chapter in this collection of patient stories focuses on actual patient encounters, and real-time, in-the-moment thinking is disclosed (*these thoughts are italicized*). Chapters are concluded with teaching points pertinent for patients or caregivers (**these lessons are bolded**) that inform the claim that patients and doctors together can accomplish far more than they can apart.

Why this format? Stories teach. Stories edify and grant insight. Stories bequeath transferable truths, but their hidden gift is much more—stories instill hope. Somehow, someway, stories instill hope.

The cumulative impact of these narratives will hopefully stir our collective spirits and ignite a fresh motivation for patients and doctors to join together to forge meaningful and lasting relationships and, in so doing, redefine the course of our health care system.

AUTHOR'S NOTE

In telling these stories I've tried to re-create the original dialogue. Copious notes have helped me greatly in this task, but the sheer amount of time and information involved in a patient encounter prevents a strict adherence to a "snapshot/tape recording" criterion of literal accuracy. While attempting to stay as close as possible to actual conversations, I have engaged in some editing in order to avoid repetition, preserve relevance, and protect patients' privacy. Some names and circumstances have been changed in order to ensure confidentiality. For the sake of readability I have elected to use the male pronoun in situations that reference both genders. I have also chosen to use the terms *physician* or *doctor* to refer to medical providers, but these references should be broadly interpreted to include nurse practitioners, physician assistants, and other caregivers as well. *Italics* represent in-the-moment thoughts arising during active engagement with the patient. **Bolded** font is used to identify the lessons—the heart of this compendium.

This book has been percolating in my brain for more than a decade. In the end it was Yoda's exhortation from *Star Wars* that served as the necessary catalyst for me to finally undertake the task of addressing the issues contained herein: "Do or do not; there is no try." I thank you for considering this endeavor.

Plain
TALK

Plain talk makes room

for disagreeable skepticism,

and, in so doing,

accepts the adversity

rooted within candor.

"Doc,
Can You
Save Her?"

"I'M HEADING OVER TO THE DOCTOR'S ROOM to do a little reading," I mumbled to the nurse after completing charts on several patients seen that morning in the emergency room. Their summer ailments had ranged from coughing and wheezing to poison ivy and diarrhea.

Making my way to the call room, I glanced down the long, poorly lit corridor and did a double take when I saw a middle-aged couple standing in the front lobby.

Good grief, get a room—this is a hospital, not a motel.

A paunchy fellow had his right hand clasped on a lady's rump and seemed oblivious to the fact that he was in a place filled with sick and suffering people. Shaking my head, I entered the austere call room and lay down on the bed to review a couple medical articles.

A few minutes later, the telephone rang and the ER nurse said, "Doctor, you have a couple of patients needing to be seen."

"Okay. I'll be over in a minute."

I strolled back to the ER, and lo and behold, there was the slightly heavy-set couple I'd seen near the information desk a few minutes earlier. The guy still appeared to be grabbing the woman's buttock with his hand, but something was odd regarding their posture. They stood together stiffly, and the lady winced when her partner shifted his stance. I briefly scanned the two charts on the countertop—Willie and Sally Bent—and introduced myself, saying, "Mr. and Mrs. Bent, I'm Dr. Scott Jensen. How can I help you?"

Willie's left arm dangled as if it were bored and didn't know what to do. Sally hunched forward slightly and leaned into her husband's right side. A long pause ensued. Finally Willie muttered, "Well, Doc, we got a problem."

He's trying to smile, but he looks like he's in pain.

"All right, tell me about your problem," I said.

Another long silence, and then Sally said, "Doctor, we were fishing, and, well . . . maybe it would be best, if you just, ah, if you just took a look," and she jerked her right thumb over her shoulder a couple times to point toward her backside, looking a bit like a hitchhiker.

As the two mystery patients stood quietly next to each other, I walked around them and then blurted, "Oh, wow!" and said no more, trying to understand what had happened. I was staring at a shiny silver spoon lure with two scarlet reflective "eyes" connecting Willie's right hand to Sally's left buttock. The lure had treble hooks at both ends—intended for fish, but now tethering a couple of humans. Both treble hooks had done some damage. One hook was embedded in Willie's right palm while the other had torn through Sally's slacks and planted itself in her left buttock.

Hmmm . . . pretty bizarre fishing trip. It looks like Willie's hand got the worst of the deal. I guess he wasn't getting fresh with his wife after all.

I bent over and did a brief exam, gently moving the lure to see how much wiggle room I had to work with. This caused Willie to grunt loudly, while Sally flinched and exclaimed, "Ouch! Doc, take it easy—that hurts."

I bet it does, but it's going to hurt a lot more before it hurts less.

I straightened up, walked to the charting desk to jot a couple of notes, and then said, "Sally, you were absolutely correct. Taking a look was quicker than having you try to explain, but why don't you tell me what happened anyway."

She cleared her throat and began. "Fishing had been slow all morning, and I was a little bored, so I picked a lure out of the tackle box and asked Willie if I could try it. Maybe my luck would change."

Before she could continue, Willie rasped in an irritated voice, "Biggest mistake of the day—and it wasn't even noon. My favorite lure—the Red Eye Wiggler."

"I see," I said and waited, but following Willie's terse expression of his annoyance, neither Sally nor Willie said a word.

This is awkward.

"Please, Sally, continue. What happened next?" I encouraged.

"Well, anyway, I went to cast toward the shore, but the lure was heavier than I was used to, and I think it pulled some line off my reel during my backswing. The slack in the line let the lure reach all the way to my butt, which I snagged, and all of a sudden I felt a terrible pain. It really hurt, and I screamed. Then Willie swore at me, saying, 'What the hell did you do now?' I started crying, so he finally came over to help me. He saw I was hooked, so he told me to stand still and started fiddling around with the lure. Then, out of nowhere, a big wave hit the boat. I lost my balance and sat down to avoid falling in the river, but I landed on Willie's hand and he started cussing and hollering at me again."

"Well, who wouldn't?" Willie interjected. "My hand hurt like crazy."

"I bet it did, Willie, and I have to believe you're both still in pain. The hook in your hand is in pretty deep, and Sally's buttock already shows significant bruises. But what happened next?"

Willie said, "Doc, do I gotta draw you a picture? One end of the lure was stuck in my hand, and the other end was plugged into her butt. We were trapped together, and everything was getting bloody. It was a crummy trip to the dock trying to operate the motor and land the boat with her never more than a foot away. When we had to skedaddle across the front seat of the pickup connected to each other, she about killed me when she sat on my hand again and drove the hook in deeper yet! I screamed at her to lift her butt, and then she slammed her head into the cab roof and started crying all over again. My hand throbbed like crazy. Anyway we finally got to the hospital, parked the truck, and she sat on my hand again while getting out. I yelped and bled some more. Then when we walked into this place, it didn't take any brains to figure out everybody was looking at us and snickering."

"I'm sorry they acted like that, Willie. Sometimes people can be pretty insensitive if they don't know what really happened."

I'm sure glad he isn't able to read my mind and realize I was one of those people.

"Anyway, you're here now, so let's get you folks taken care of."

I studied the positions of Willie's right hand and Sally's left buttock and assessed the small area in which I would have to work. I cut away part of Sally's pants, isolating the hook and exposing the wound.

Those hooks are in deep. Not a lot of working room. Hmmm . . . I doubt there's any way I can disconnect Willie and Sally without ruining the—what did Willie call it?—the Red Eye Wiggler.

While I was considering how best to extract the hooks without further injuring the hand and buttock, Willie interrupted my train of thought. "Doc, can you save her?"

Engrossed in my work, I wasn't sure I heard him right. "Pardon me?" I said without looking away from the problem at hand.

"Can you save her?" Willie repeated. His tone was full of love and concern.

Hmmm . . . That's a surprise. It's nice to hear Willie is worried about Sally's welfare.

I glanced at him and said, "Willie, let me put your mind at ease. Sally is going to be just fine. She's in no danger, and the scar will be tiny."

A few moments had passed when Sally giggled and said, "Dr. Jensen, he's talking about the fishing lure, not me."

And then I could hold back no longer. I stood up and laughed out loud. "Willie, I am sorry, but no, I will not be able to salvage the lure. You can have the spoon back, but the hooks will be gone. I have to clip them off so I can separate you two."

In a flat voice expressing little conviction, Willie replied, "Oh, I see. I guess ya gotta do what ya gotta do . . . I suppose."

You really don't want me doing this without separating the two of you, Willie. Trust me on this.

Frustrated, Willie snarled at Sally. "Next time, just drop the line in the water, and we can troll so you don't have to do any casting."

I can't believe that less than an hour ago I thought these folks were ill-behaved lovebirds engaging in juvenile displays of public affection.

Further conversation seemed pointless, so I had the nurse get things ready. I positioned Willie and Sally so that they bent over a gurney while I began my task. I snipped the hooks from the spoon and separated my tethered patients. Then I tended to Willie because manipulating his hand had caused his wound to start oozing blood. After injecting novocaine, I removed the embedded hook and applied antibiotic ointment and bandaged his hand.

I treated Sally's buttock similarly and announced, "Okay, we're all done. You'll both heal up as good as new."

"Thanks, Doc. Sure do 'preciate your help," Willie said in a resigned tone.

"Willie, I'm sorry about your lure. Here it is." I handed him the naked silver spoon that now looked somewhat like a miniature ice cream scoop.

I heard Sally snicker when she glanced down at the ruined lure so tenderly cradled in his bandaged hand. Willie glared at her, and I figured it was definitely time to say farewell.

So long, Willie, and don't be too hard on Sally. She meant no harm, and I'm sure she'll think twice before asking to use anything from your tackle box. As for me, I will forever remember your story as the one in which I saved a wife but not the Red Eye Wiggler.

🐟 🐟 🐟

MANY YEARS LATER, I was reminded of Willie and his fishing lure when a forty-three-year-old patient came to see me for a routine checkup on a chilly November afternoon. When I had first told Carter that he had diabetes four years earlier, he was understandably upset, but he quickly learned how to manage his disease. My nurse showed him how to prick his finger for sugar testing and how to inject insulin. I taught him to count carbs and how to calculate insulin coverage for whatever he ate or drank, whether it was a cheeseburger, a beer, or a banana. Carter learned much, asked questions, chuckled occasionally, and flourished in the face of a potentially serious health issue.

We saw each other often, and our relationship grew. Together we tackled numerous diabetic issues and routinely discussed potential complications. He became proficient at checking his sugar levels and calculating how much insulin to inject. I was a mere phone call away, and he was comforted by this ready access.

Assembly-line health care is driven by an appetite for profit and power and doesn't pay much attention to relationship-building.

But on this wintry day I walked into the exam room and was met with a furrowed brow. There was a catch in his voice as Carter blurted, "Doc, I don't know how to tell you this, but I have to change doctors!" His voice was a little hoarse, and he seemed on the verge of tears.

"Okay, Carter, tell me what's happened."

He cut to the chase. "Well, you know our family gets our health insurance through my wife's job. Last week Clare found out there were some changes for next year. In order to save money, her employer worked with an insurance company and a hospital care system to put a plan together for the employees. Your clinic isn't in the network, so I can't see you after the first of the year. Clare's boss told her there was no choice in the matter. When Clare told me, I was angry and reminded her that you were the one who diagnosed me with diabetes and helped me get through all the struggles with the pills and insulin. She agreed and was upset, but said there was nothing she could do—her employer had made the decision, and it was final. Doc, this just isn't fair. You and I have worked hard together, and we know each other. We have a relationship—shouldn't that count for something?"

I had no answer, but Carter was correct. Our clinic had been carved out of the picture by an employer/hospital/insurance alliance, and it had nothing to do with quality of care or patient choice. I was disappointed, but I knew this outcome was possible because the business of health care had changed dramatically and countless government and insurance regulations had diminished the patient's decision-making role. Like Carter, I was frustrated because patient-doctor bonds built on trust and advocacy no longer seemed to carry much sway.

Patients such as Carter are being forced to abandon long-standing relationships with doctors because the big players in the health care scene are manipulating the system for more dollars, more patients, and more control.

"Carter, a new day has dawned in the world of medical care, and your concerns aren't as important as they used to be—and neither are mine. Our relationship represents significant investment on both our parts. You trust me and know that I take seriously my role as your advocate. I believe in you and appreciate your commitment to maintaining your good health. Our bond is critical to the work we do together, and it didn't happen overnight. It's sad to say but today's world of **assembly-line health care is driven by an appetite for profit and power and doesn't pay much attention to relationship-building.** I'll miss you. I'm sorry."

Our visit was over, and soon, once his transfer of records was complete, our bond would wither.

☙ ☙ ☙

THAT NIGHT, as I lay in bed trying to sleep, my mind kept coming back to Carter and his departure from our clinic. I mulled over what he had said about our journey together working to get his diabetes under control. I was irritated that our relationship could so casually be dismissed as if its vital components—trust and advocacy—were of no consequence.

And then, with startling clarity, a novel thought took shape.

Clare's employer—in concert with an insurance company and hospital-clinic network—took the connection Carter and I built and cut away its essential elements: Carter's trust in me was discarded, and my advocacy for his well-being was ignored. I perceived a haunting parallel between this corporate neutering of a meaningful patient-doctor relationship and my own actions twenty years earlier when I clipped and threw away the two hooks of a lure, terminating its usefulness by removing that which gave it meaning.

Can a patient-doctor connection be cleaved as casually as a Red Eye Wiggler?

As I finally surrendered to sleep, I was hounded by nightmarish dreams, surreal and disturbing, and I encountered Willie at the front end of a long line of patients. He looked at me quizzically and asked, "Can you save her?" In my muddled state, I could not tell if his concern was for the cherished Red Eye Wiggler or the bond patients and doctors once shared.

CRISIS

AT

37,000 FEET

THE FLIGHT HOME started uneventfully enough. We left on time and experienced no significant turbulence en route. But when the request came over the PA sound system, "Would any medical personnel please report to the kitchen galley at the front of the plane," everything changed. As I walked to the front of the Boeing 737, I wondered, *What will this be about?*

A couple minutes later, brief introductions took place just outside a tiny bathroom stall behind the cockpit as the flight attendant, Jane, acquainted me with Elizabeth, and her niece, Jillian. Elizabeth told me that her husband, Robert, had not been feeling well, so she and Jillian had helped him into the bathroom, where he had collapsed onto the closed toilet seat. I stepped partway into the cubicle to check on him and found a medium-built elderly man, hugging himself and moaning softly. He didn't answer my questions, and his eyes were glassing over. I needed to get him out of the bathroom and onto the floor where I could better assess the situation.

Sudden turbulence knocked me into the doorjamb, and I saw Jane help Elizabeth and Jillian to their seats ten feet away. Jane and I then gently extracted Robert from the tiny compartment. His body was dead weight, and he seemed unaware of our efforts. Grunting and straining, we finally got him into the galley and positioned him on his back with pillows under his feet and head.

The realization that the folks in the first-class section were mesmerized by our efforts dawned on me, and I figured they were intrigued by this close-up version of reality TV. I asked Jane for a blood pressure cuff, stethoscope, oxygen tank, mask, and automatic external defibrillator (AED, a portable electronic device capable of diagnosing and treating life-threatening rhythm disturbances of the heart).

Over the next few minutes, my examination revealed a slow heart rate in the thirties and wheezing in both lungs, leading to the conclusion that Robert was struggling to get oxygenated blood to his vital organs—heart, brain, kidneys. His abdomen was soft without apparent tenderness, reassuring me that he was not bleeding internally. But he was virtually comatose.

He's probably had a heart attack. I wish I could check his blood for oxygen and sugar levels.

The flight attendant produced the items I had requested, and a nurse appeared at my side, volunteering to help. She applied an oxygen mask to Robert's nose and mouth and adjusted the oxygen concentration to the maximum level. Robert's own breathing efforts were marginal at best, and he definitely needed some help—maybe more than we could provide.

Good grief, this guy might die before the plane lands. We're almost an hour away from Minneapolis, and he's getting worse.

I was confident he felt no pain, but his distressed breathing was alarming, with barely a whisper of air moving in and out of his lungs. His pulse was weak and irregular. Jane powered up the AED device, I applied the paddles to his chest, and the monitor's toneless mechanical voice pronounced its verdict: "Do not shock," meaning that no heart rhythms responsive to electric shock had been identified by this electronic brain, and it would refuse to do anything. Robert was fading fast, and I had scant tools or equipment with which to deal with this crisis. There were no instruments available to check oxygen or sugar levels, and I had in my possession all known medical equipment on the plane.

I need to speak with Elizabeth and Jillian and prepare them for the worst.

I went to Elizabeth and advised her that Robert was gravely ill and asked if she could give me any more information. She told me that he was eighty-five years old, and they had been married for more than sixty years. A couple hours into the flight he had begun to feel weak and queasy, so he thought he should go to the bathroom. Elizabeth and Jillian had just gotten him into the restroom when he suddenly started breathing hard and groaned, slumping onto the commode.

Elizabeth showed me a list of Robert's medications, and I reviewed them quickly. She told me he suffered from lung disease. I considered the facts at hand and drew some conclusions.

"Elizabeth, Jillian, it hurts me to tell you this, but I think Robert has suffered a heart attack, and he may not recover."

Elizabeth choked on her words. "Please, Doctor, please do whatever you can to help him."

"I will," I said quietly.

Her entreaty ringing in my ears, I returned to Robert's side and noticed that beads of sweat had appeared on his forehead and his color was turning an ashen gray. His lips were bluish. My brain churned at a hundred miles an hour as I rapidly reappraised the situation, deliberated on my options, and considered the unpleasant but likely conclusion to this crisis. The nurse and I quietly conferred, coming up with no new ideas as to how to help Robert.

We are helpless to help him. I wish we could do something, anything to increase his chances for survival.

I crouched on the floor of the galley, gently shook Robert, and asked if he could hear me. There was no response. I pinched the skin on his upper chest, looking for any kind of response to pain; there was none. His breathing was shallow with occasional gasps; his pulse was thready and irregular and had slowed further; it was now in the twenties and certainly inadequate for life-sustaining circulation.

Am I missing anything? Has he already suffered brain damage? If there's nothing I can do now, what will I do if he gets worse? I need to talk to Elizabeth and see what she wants me to do if his heart stops or he quits breathing. Will she want me to be aggressive and start CPR? Or will she decline heroic interventions?

I considered my choices; they were few, and none of them were attractive. I glanced at Elizabeth in her seat and again noticed the entire first-class section craning forward, watching and listening with a mixture of fascination and apprehension. I whispered to the flight attendant, "How long to landing?" She murmured, "Fifteen or twenty minutes." I asked her to advise the pilot that an emergency crew might be needed at the gateway.

With the flight attendant on the phone to the pilot and the nurse at Robert's side, I returned to Elizabeth and Jillian. "Robert's lost consciousness. His heart may stop beating in the next few minutes. His breathing is irregular and ineffective. He's not in any pain."

Elizabeth responded, "I can't believe this is happening." She wept quietly, and I was freshly disappointed by my inability to do anything to help this gracious lady. Her world had turned upside down in a hurry.

"Robert's not suffering; he feels no distress. But I do think he's leaving us," I whispered.

Jillian's eyes were wet with tears, and she slowly nodded her head in understanding. Jane hovered nearby, seemingly paralyzed with emotion, waiting for me to give some sort of instruction. After a few moments passed, I asked Elizabeth, "Do you want me to start CPR if Robert's heart or lungs stop? I need some guidance from you."

An eerie absence of noise hung over the first-class cabin; the air seemed dense and foreboding. Time stood still until finally Jillian asked me, "What do you think we should do?"

"There's no one right decision. If we start CPR and can keep him alive, the paramedics will meet us at the airport, transport him to a hospital, and try to stabilize him with an airway tube, intravenous lines, and possibly a ventilator to keep him breathing. Heroic measures might be able to maintain heart rate and respirations, but the status of his brain is a huge question mark. Significant injury may already have occurred."

Time passed. I looked Elizabeth straight in the eye and said, "Do you want me to begin chest compressions and start breathing for Robert if it becomes necessary?" It was painful to watch her facial expressions as she wrestled with this horrendous yes or no decision.

Elizabeth looked at Jillian and said quietly, "He wouldn't want that." Tears ran down her cheeks. Stillness enclosed our world, and the impact of her confession suspended any interruptions. I ached for this lady and cursed my impotence. Before getting on this plane her world was intact; now nothing was normal—everything was tainted by the exquisite fear that someone terribly dear was leaving forever.

Elizabeth trembled and realized her words—"He wouldn't want that"—were, in fact, her answer. Silence hung in the air. It was as if she had uttered her decision, and it was now irretrievable.

Jillian nodded her support, and her voice was hoarse with emotion. "You're right, he wouldn't want that." She seemed awestruck by her agreement with Elizabeth.

They both looked at me, ineffable sadness in their eyes, tears flowing, lips quivering, and together they slowly shook their heads. Elizabeth solemnly declared, "We don't want you to do that to him."

The air grew hot, sullied by the oppressive sadness. It defied normal breathing. Trying to swallow over the lump in my throat was painful, and my vision clouded with tears. I lowered my eyes and quietly said, "I understand. Robert will not be uncomfortable; his dignity will be respected."

Little did I realize the challenge coming my way regarding that simple pledge.

I returned to Robert and reevaluated his status. He was quiet, and his chest was motionless for seconds at a time. I opened his eyes and touched the corneas with a Kleenex. There was no hint of a blink. He was leaving us. I wiped away the saliva at the corner of his mouth. Gazing around the tiny galley—the open restroom door, the medical gear strewn about, the stethoscope on the floor—I felt absolutely powerless.

Incredible. A woman becomes a widow on an airplane ride that was supposed to be just another routine trip home. She and her husband were simply doing what they have done many times before.

The touch of death heightens our awareness of the flimsy balance by which we are sustained in this world.

I prayed for wisdom I did not possess, knowing what the coming minutes would demand as I attended to Elizabeth and Jillian.

Kneeling next to Robert, I watched for any changes. Minimal movements were occasionally present—a twitch, a jerk, a gasp—otherwise nothing. I went back to Elizabeth and Jillian and said, "He's in no pain. Do you have any questions?"

They shook their heads and silently dropped their chins to their chests. During the next few minutes, I stayed next to Robert and saw only the occasional heaving of his chest muscles. The nurse retired to her seat.

I should get some sort of documentation that Robert's family declined intervention with CPR.

I pulled Jane aside and advised her that Elizabeth and Jillian should sign a form indicating that they had declined CPR.

Her eyes widened and she blurted, "That's a good thought. You're right."

She took two steps from me, then circled back with a confused look on her face. "I guess I don't know how to do that. We don't have any forms. Can you help me with that?"

I handwrote a note stating that after medical assessment and treatment had been accomplished, Elizabeth and her niece had declined CPR for Robert. As Elizabeth and her niece were signing this document, Robert's leg muscles contracted and twitched in a slow dance of death. I went to him. It seemed especially cruel that here at 37,000 feet, the buffeting winds and turbulence would confine Elizabeth and Jillian to their seats, keeping them from being at his side.

Robert was finally still. His chest revealed no movement. He had no blood pressure. No pulse could be found—nothing at the wrist, nothing at the carotids, and finally, even with the stethoscope, no audible heart sounds and no respiratory noises. Robert was dead. I told Elizabeth and Jillian.

◻ ◻ ◻

A FEW MINUTES LATER, as the sun set on the western horizon, the plane entered its final approach and eased into a landing devoid of any drama other than the *bump, bump* of the wheels. Lost in my thoughts of death and loss and fragile hearts and tears, I barely noticed that the subdued passengers were all buckled in and Jane was perched in her jump seat, anxiously twisting her wedding band. And me—I was drained, trying to stay put while the decelerating plane spent its velocity. I knelt next to Robert's blanketed body, keeping this man I barely knew secure and protected. We were home.

I heard and felt the thump of the gateway against the airplane, and a crisp knock followed. Jane opened the door, and before it was even fully open, six men and women in medical uniforms rushed in with the lead person barking orders, calling for a gurney, demanding a defibrillator, and preparing to start CPR. I stepped near him as he instructed the first-class passengers to remain in their seats and quietly advised him that Robert was dead and that CPR was not necessary.

With a surprised expression, this paramedic barked at me, "What do you mean? What are you talking about?"

I responded, "I pronounced him dead about ten minutes ago."

"We've still got a chance then," he snapped. He ignored me and turned to his colleagues. "Let's get moving. Time's short."

I interjected, "No, please don't. The family doesn't want that. They declined any heroic efforts, including CPR."

He snarled at me. "Listen up, whoever you are: that's not what we're here for, and I don't make that kind of decision. We need to get to work—now! The doctors can sort things out later, if we can get him stabilized and to the hospital—and right now, that's a big if!"

I looked at him, surprised and insulted. I hoped Elizabeth and Jillian couldn't hear this exchange, but I had had my fill of this John Wayne character with his in-your-face attitude. I hissed in a barely audible tone, "Look, I'm a doctor, and I took care of this gentleman for the last hour. I did what I could, but he's dead, and the family not only declined CPR or heroic measures, they signed a note indicating the same."

On hearing that a signed document existed, he fixed me with an icy stare and, for the first time, seemed to actually regard me as someone who might have something worthwhile to say. He asked, "Do you have this document?"

"Yes." I pulled the paper out of my pocket and showed it to him. His face went blank, and he turned away sheepishly. The mood in the little galley area suddenly switched from hectic to subdued, and this turn of events quickly brought about a reordering of priorities: the obnoxious blinking lights of the nearby emergency vehicles were doused, the uniformed personnel withdrew into the background, and the gateway was cleared.

Robert's cooling body was slowly and respectfully placed on a backboard, and he was carried down some stairs to an ambulance. Elizabeth and Jillian followed the paramedics; I was pulled aside and questioned by police and security personnel about details and time sequences; and finally the passengers were allowed to disembark.

While the travelers passed me in the gateway, many interrupted the officers' interrogation to thank me for my efforts. Later, a man approached me at the baggage carousel to tell me that he had covered me in prayer during the entire episode. I quietly nodded my appreciation.

My earlier reflection on treating the thunderstruck first-class passengers to a bird's-eye view of a tragic in-air emergency had come full circle. It seemed odd. During the flight, these folks were stunned into quietness, and I was the man in action. Now I was the one who was dazed, trying to process all that had happened. I felt an odd sense of vulnerability, perhaps born of my inadequacy to help Robert. I even felt fragile, as if I might break down. And here were my fellow passengers—now they were in motion—reacting to the crisis with handshakes and supportive acknowledgments of my efforts. They fortified me.

֍ ֍ ֍

TWO MONTHS AFTER THE DRAMA IN THE SKY, I was sitting on the third-base line during the seventh inning of a Minnesota Twins game. Hungry, I left my seat to get a hot dog. Walking along an aisle bordering a row of seats, I noticed a young woman looking at me. She had a child on each side of her, and it appeared that her husband was next to one of the kids. She made eye contact with me, and I smiled as I moved past her. For whatever reason, I glanced back and noticed that she was still staring at me, so I stopped, retraced a few steps, and asked her if we had ever met.

She stood and said, "Yes. I think you were on a flight from California back to Minnesota a few weeks ago. Is that true?"

Hesitantly I said, "Well, yes."

Before anything else could be said, her impatient daughter, maybe seven years old, interrupted with a tug on her jacket, saying, "Who is that, Mommy? Who is that strange man?"

The woman seemed lost in thought and memory. She momentarily stared off into the distance, glanced back at me once again, looked at her daughter, and said in a broken voice, "He is the man who was a hero and took care of a sick person on the airplane. He is a doctor and was very kind."

I was taken aback and more than a little astonished. Haltingly I told the woman that she had a good memory, and I thanked her for her compliment.

She looked me straight in the eye, shook her head, and said, "No, you don't need to thank me. I saw what you did. I thank you for what you did. And I will never forget . . . what you did."

We shared awkward good-byes, and I walked away—stunned and reflective.

Sometimes we touch others in ways we couldn't possibly imagine. Incredible! Who could have guessed, after two months and in a stadium filled with forty thousand people, this woman would pull me back to that plane ride and then thank me with such remarkable poignancy. We really never know when we might be given the chance to reach out and impact the hearts and minds of others.

I was profoundly moved, and silently I prayed:

Thank you, God, for the privilege to be a physician.

≥ ≥ ≥

ON A ROUTINE FLIGHT HOME a life ended, leaving behind some powerful messages. **Life is a fragile gift.** Seven miles above good old terra firma, some prayed, some murmured quiet incantations, and many were simply spellbound, watching a fellow human endure the journey culminating in his death—before their very eyes. The touch of death heightens our awareness of the flimsy balance by which we are sustained in this world. Robert's abrupt departure at 37,000 feet was a catalyst for many to feel anew the raw emotions death riles up in all of us. To paraphrase John Donne, "No man is an island . . . we are all diminished."

Within the mysterious walk of everyday life, we are all confronted with startling opportunities to see grace in action. I had the chance to experience Elizabeth's dignity and strength in a time of immeasurable sadness. She would not be forgotten.

I was reminded of the important lesson that **just because the immediate crisis is over doesn't mean another predicament isn't lurking nearby.** I had no idea that the issue of CPR and heroic efforts would still hang in the balance when Robert's body and I were suddenly surrounded by six people committed to action and sending a strong nonverbal message: "We're here, so step aside and let the professionals handle this!" I was immensely thankful that the idea of having Elizabeth and Jillian sign a hand-scribbled note indicating their rejection of CPR had crossed my mind.

And finally, the improbable sharing at the baseball game—two months after the fact—from a woman in the first-class section of the plane reminded me that **humans touch one another in inconceivable ways.** Her words left me with a sense of hallowed awareness that serving others is indeed a privilege of the highest order.

We really never know

when we might be given the chance

to reach out and impact

the hearts and minds of others.

The Prescription
That Should
Not
Have Been

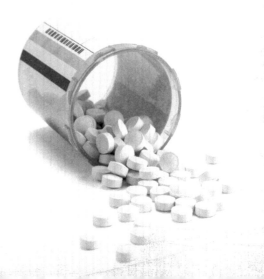

ERTRUDE VISITED OUR CLINIC occasionally—perhaps once a year. I walked into the exam room and there she sat, frowning and fidgety.

Something's bothering Gertrude. I wonder what's going on.

"Gertrude, how can I help you today?"

"Dr. Jensen, I'm a little concerned. I've been having some chest pains, and lately they've been more bothersome. Maybe I should have come in sooner."

Her confession spoke volumes about the gravity of her concern.

"Okay, tell me more about your pain. When does it occur, and is there anything you can do to make it go away?"

"Well, for the last couple of months, if I exert myself, I feel a pressure in my chest. If I stop and rest, it goes away."

"Do you notice any other symptoms when you have this pain?"

"Not really. Maybe there's a little discomfort in my neck once in a while, but not every time. Sometimes I feel a little short on wind when the pain hits."

Hmmm . . . what to do? Gertrude may be in her eighties, but she's as healthy as a sixty-year-old. She lives independently, rakes her own leaves, cleans her own home, shovels her own snow, and enjoys hosting family holiday meals. She's got a lot to live for. I need to figure out what's going on, but the tests I want to order pose significant risk for her.

After asking a lot of questions and completing an examination and electrocardiogram, I told Gertrude, "I'm concerned that your chest pain may be caused by blockage in the arteries supplying your heart. I think we need to look into this aggressively."

Gertrude listened carefully but said not a word.

I continued, "I want to order an angiogram. Now, I don't make a habit of ordering angiograms for patients in their eighties because of the risks involved with the procedure. But you're pretty unusual, Gertrude. You show absolutely no sign of slowing down. The problem is your symptoms are highly suspicious for angina—a heart pain caused by a lack of blood flow usually due to obstruction—and this is a life-threatening issue. Even though an angiogram can cause a heart attack or stroke during the procedure itself, I do think you should undergo the test. With your permission, I'd like to call a cardiologist and get it scheduled as soon as possible."

I watched her closely and gauged the impact of my words.

Shaking her head, she said, "I don't know; it sounds a little scary. I'm pretty old and getting frail, but if you think I should—well, I guess, I suppose I'll do it."

"Thanks, Gertrude. The test is used to identify blockage by injecting a dye into the blood vessels of your heart. If plugged arteries are seen during the procedure, the cardiologist can often solve the problem right then and there by inserting a stent into the

Do we have to start getting sued for problems stemming from unnecessary prescribing before we change our habits?

culprit vessel and restoring the blood flow. The results can be impressive, and in your situation the potential benefit of eliminating your symptoms without lots of pills or open-heart surgery would be immense."

She looked at me and slowly nodded her head, saying, "Okay."

I called Dr. Wayne Anderson, a highly regarded heart specialist, and shared Gertrude's story. I told him I did not usually order angiograms for patients in their ninth decade of life, but in this case I thought it would be best, due to Gertrude's remarkable youthfulness. If blockages were identified and stents placed, Gertrude might live productively and independently for a long time to come. Dr. Anderson agreed with my assessment and indicated he would make the arrangements.

The morning after the procedure, Dr. Anderson called with the results. "Dr. Jensen, I'm a little embarrassed that we even did the angiogram. I definitely expected to find something, but Gertrude's coronary arteries are clean as a whistle."

I replied, "That surprises me, too, but I'm sure glad to hear it. I know it will ease Gertrude's mind. Thanks for getting it done."

Just as I was about to hang up, he added, "Oh, by the way, her cholesterol was a little high, so I put her on Lipitor and asked her to recheck with you in a month."

I said nothing. A long pause ensued.

"Dr. Jensen, are you still there?"

"Yes, I am."

"I thought I lost you there."

With an edge in my voice, I replied, "Well, you did—lose me, that is."

"What do you mean?" he asked.

"I'm trying to figure out why you put Gertrude on Lipitor when you just got done telling me that her coronary arteries are, to use your words, 'clean as a whistle.' I don't understand that."

"Well, her cholesterol was too high."

(Lipitor, a prescription medication used to lower cholesterol, is one of a family of drugs called "statins." Statins are prescribed often and are effective in lowering cholesterol, but they also have significant side effects.)

There is no way Dr. Anderson can know how strongly I believe doctors prescribe too many pills, and far too casually. Unfortunately for him, he just pricked one of my major pet peeves.

Before I fully realized what I was saying, I blurted out, "Dr. Anderson, you just told me that after eighty-six years of life her coronary vessels are fine. The angiogram demonstrated that there was no significant blockage, regardless of what her cholesterol numbers have been for nearly a century. Her chest pain was not related to any cholesterol plaques. So what do you really expect to accomplish by starting Lipitor at this point in her life? She's probably more likely to develop side effects than receive any real benefit. Do you really think that was a good move?"

"Her numbers were a little high," he replied hotly. "I thought a candidate for an angiogram would be a candidate for a cholesterol-lowering drug."

"I think you reacted to a number and forgot about my patient."

Silence took over, until he said quietly, "Well, I guess we just disagree on this. You can always stop the Lipitor when she follows up with you."

"You can bet on that" was my pointed response, and I knew our professional relationship would never be the same.

I can't believe he prescribed Lipitor for her. That just makes no sense. What will it take for doctors to stop writing so many prescriptions? Do we have to start getting sued for problems stemming from unnecessary prescribing before we change our habits?

◈ ◈ ◈

I THOUGHT OF ANOTHER PATIENT, Ralph, a man in his late eighties who suffered a stroke during open-heart surgery for a coronary artery bypass. A year later a consulting physician started him on testosterone injections because he had discovered Ralph to have a "low T" value (that is, a low level of the male hormone testosterone). Despite the fact that Ralph was already on several high-risk drugs for his heart, including a blood thinner, this consultant prescribed testosterone even though it had been linked to accelerating heart problems. Ralph was a poor candidate for this drug due to his advanced age, critical medical problems, and multiple pills already on board; testosterone injections were a dangerous intervention for Ralph with little likelihood for benefit.

I am flabbergasted by the love affair doctors have with their prescription pads.

I believe both Gertrude and Ralph were victims of "scientific bullying"— not an uncommon practice in the world of Western medicine. I thought about what happens when "the expert" (doctor) presumes an intellectual superiority to convince "the audience" (patient) to make the "correct" decision. Patients are often inclined to passively go along with the doctor's suggestion even though they don't think it's necessary or a good idea.

I wonder how often I claim this intellectual authority. Is it sometimes necessary in order to help a patient make a decision in complex situations? I certainly can't explain every possible outcome for every drug or procedure. Do I even realize when I cross the line into "bullying" territory? Is it reasonable to expect patients to sort through complicated and potentially lethal treatment options—surgery, drugs, chemotherapy, or radiation—without a nudge in one direction or another? Or am I just rationalizing my behavior when I find it convenient to pressure a patient into a decision that suits my purposes?

ꙮ ꙮ ꙮ

A COUPLE WEEKS LATER, Gertrude came in for her follow-up visit, and before I even had a chance to sit down, she complained, "I hope this Lipitor isn't really necessary. I hate to disagree with the heart doctor, but I decided not to take it until I talked to you. You're my doctor, and I trust you. I'm not comfortable adding another pill unless you tell me I should."

She described her encounter with Dr. Anderson and how she felt compelled to follow his advice but wanted to consult with me first.

"Gertrude, I'm sorry Dr. Anderson prescribed that drug. He's a good doctor, and he did a nice job of helping us determine that your heart vessels are not obstructed. But doctors don't always agree. We each have our own viewpoint as to what's important. In this case, I disagree with his decision to prescribe Lipitor for you, but many doctors would do exactly as he did. Lipitor has been a great drug for lots of folks, but it isn't for everyone."

Gertrude interrupted. "But I'm closing in on ninety. I don't want more pills."

"I understand where you're coming from, Gertrude. I really do. But there are lots of issues like this in medicine, whether it be pills, surgeries, supplements, vaccines, or even foods. On these matters there is no clearly established correct answer. Doctors often debate the value of flu shots, the danger of eating eggs, the risk of sun exposure, or the problem with grapefruit juice. That's just the way it is."

I paused, but Gertrude remained quiet. She was obviously thinking about something I'd said.

I continued, "So please don't be offended by Dr. Anderson's prescription for Lipitor. He's simply used to pulling out his prescription pad if the cholesterol number is higher than he likes."

She nodded. "Dr. Jensen, I understand that doctors don't always see eye to eye. But what you just said about eggs and grapefruit juice got me thinking. I guess I'm not a very good patient: I eat eggs almost every day, and I really like my grapefruit juice."

Chuckling, I said, "Good for you, Gertrude, and I think you're a terrific patient. I'm not worried about what you eat for breakfast, but I do think you're having occasional muscle spasms in your esophagus, which is the connecting tube between your mouth and stomach. Contractions in this area can feel just like heart pains. I want you to try some antacid if it happens again and keep an eye out for anything that might trigger your symptoms, such as caffeine, carbonated beverages, or spicy foods. And to get back to your question, Gertrude, no, you don't have to take the Lipitor; I wouldn't. After eighty-six years the arteries supplying your heart are wide open and doing their job—that's what the angiogram told us. I don't think doctors or Lipitor are going to improve on that track record. That is one prescription that should not have been written."

≥ ≥ ≥

MEDICAL DECISION-MAKING in the new millennium must include patients as fully participative partners working with doctors in the process of planning and carrying out interventions. As much as physicians are inclined to judge their own perspective as the superior one, this is often not the case. My colleagues and I are susceptible to being too easily swayed by the marketing prowess of pharmaceutical companies, the promise of new-fangled technologies, and even our own passionate desire to "save the day" for our patients. The fact of the matter is that sometimes there is no day to be saved, and often pills, procedures, and devices are recommended without a full accounting of the risks involved. It is an unfortunate reality that misguided intercessions are now commonplace and perhaps inevitable considering the availability of so many options and the persuasive ploys used to advertise them. **Never before has good medical care been so in need of patient input.**

Patients must realize that today's world of health care is full of disagreements between doctors, hospitals, auditing organizations, insurance companies, and pharmaceutical corporations regarding which standard of care or recommendation is best suited for individual patient needs.

Even though patients may find it difficult to decline the well-intentioned recommendation of a doctor, they need to value their own instincts. A medication can bring about benefit or harm, and if harm is the result, stopping the drug does not always reverse the damage. Presently the United States accounts for only five percent of the world's population, but its citizens consume over half of all prescription drugs, giving testimony to the claim that a virtual epidemic of "pill-popping" has become the new reality.

DOCTORS CAN WALK AWAY

FROM THE ADVERSE IMPACTS

OF PILLS THEY PRESCRIBE—

PATIENTS MAY NOT.

"THAT'S WHAT
I'VE
BEEN TRYING
TO TELL YOU!"

I<small>T WAS A BUSY</small> S<small>ATURDAY NIGHT</small> in a downtown metropolitan hospital, and the emergency room was humming. The rooms were full, and the waiting room was bursting at the seams. Shouts, groans, and cries of all kinds could be heard, along with the occasional intercom announcement advising, "X-ray to emergency room, x-ray to emergency room."

Amidst this cacophony of sounds and smells and people, a frazzled nurse walked up to me and said, "Dr. Jensen, would you please go see the man in room 2C right away? He isn't making any sense. He seems fine and won't tell me what's wrong. He just keeps saying his guts fell out."

I smiled and nodded. "No problem, Shirley. I'll take care of it. Just give me the chart, please."

I went to room 2C, where a man in his mid-seventies was sitting quietly in no apparent discomfort. He wore a black suit coat over a white shirt with black pants and black shoes, and he was perched on the edge of the gurney with his hands folded in his lap.

"Hello, Mr. Jones. I'm Dr. Scott Jensen, and I'll be taking care of you tonight. What can I do for you?"

I wasn't sure whether he'd heard me at first, as Mr. Jones did not respond and seemed inclined to look everywhere but at my face. Finally, just as I was beginning to wonder whether I should repeat myself, he turned his eyes to me and mumbled slowly, "Well, Doc, that's the thing. I don't know how to say it, but I was on the john tonight and my guts fell out."

Hmmm . . . he probably had a hemorrhoid fall out [a protruding dilated vein in the anal area]. That can be pretty alarming if it's the first time it ever happened.

"Has this happened before?" I asked.

He smiled slightly and, sighing a little, said ever so ploddingly, "Come on, Doc, how many times do you think a guy could have his guts fall out? Maybe I pushed too hard. You probably should just take a look."

He seems like a straight shooter. Maybe he just doesn't get medical jargon. I better keep things moving, see if he has anything else to say, and try to figure out what's going on. I can take care of a hemorrhoid quickly and get back to my patient in room one.

"Mr. Jones, did you have any bleeding when this happened?"

"Funny thing, Doc," he drawled. "There was none, and I sort of thought there should have been."

"Did you feel any pain when it happened?"

"That struck me peculiar too, Doc. No pain at all. Not even a little bit," he replied, seeming to pronounce each word bit by bit.

How can this guy talk so slow? This is painful.

"Do you take any medications, Mr. Jones?"

"Nope. Don't believe in 'em," he said, as if I had asked a religious question.

This is getting nowhere fast. I've got to get moving.

I asked a couple of perfunctory questions about his medical history that netted me nothing. It just didn't seem like we were connecting. I had had enough. It was time to do an exam.

"Mr. Jones, if you could please take off your suit coat and remove your shirt, I'll just check you over a bit."

I first examined his eyes, ears, and throat, and everything was in order. Finally he slipped off his suit coat, placing it at his side, and began unbuttoning his shirt. Waiting impatiently to listen to his lungs, I watched Mr. Jones finish with the lower buttons and tug at his shirt. The instant his shirt was freed from his trousers, his intestines lurched forward, first spilling on his lap and then tumbling to the floor.

"Good grief, Mr. Jones! Your guts fell out!" I gasped.

"That's what I've been trying to tell you, Doc."

Stunned, I momentarily stared at him sitting there ever so comfortably on the edge of the gurney with his shirt wide open and his intestines hanging out of his belly, dangling over his legs, and touching the floor.

Incredible.

Then, I quickly helped him lie down in a comfortable position on his back. Grabbing some towels and donning sterile gloves, I clumsily scooped up his wiggling innards, arranging them on his abdomen in such a way that they would stay put and not fall back on the floor. Mr. Jones seemed none the worse for wear, and after a couple of deep breaths, I looked him straight in the eye and said, "I guess your problem isn't hemorrhoids."

He smiled and said, "Don't know for sure what you doctors would call it, but the problem's plain to see."

"It sure is," I said in disbelief.

I checked to make sure he was comfortable and then completed an examination. I was confident that Mr. Jones's major problem had been uncovered. Amazingly his blood pressure and pulse were spot-on normal and his heart and lungs revealed nothing out of the ordinary. I called Shirley for some sterile saline-soaked towels, ordered some lab tests, and inserted an intravenous line for fluid replenishment.

When Shirley saw the mound of intestines lying on Mr. Jones's abdomen, she doted on him with an attentiveness likely born of guilt because she had so casually dismissed his complaint earlier.

Shirley need not berate herself. There was no way for her to know what Mr. Jones had in store for us.

Jumping to a conclusion I think most logical is a crime I have committed more than once, and I would like to give up that habit.

Eventually I returned to Mr. Jones's bedside, chart in hand, and said, "Okay, Mr. Jones, let's hear it—the rest of the story."

He explained that two weeks earlier, he had had an aneurysm of his abdominal aorta repaired, and the incision had extended from his breastbone to his pubic area. He spent three uneventful days in the hospital, but during the first week at home he felt a little bloated, and sometimes things seemed to slosh around inside his belly. He was reassured by the fact that his incision looked good and figured everything was healing okay.

"Well, Doc, I was sitting on the commode a couple hours ago and thought I would feel a whole lot better if I could just get my bowels moving, and so I pushed, probably harder than I should have. The next thing I know I felt something give, and I looked down to see my guts spilling all over my legs onto the floor. It was a mess, but I tried to get presentable to come to the emergency room. Do you think you could maybe get ahold of Dr. Dasher and see if he would be willing to fix me up?"

Wow, this guy has a big incision slowly break down from the inside-out and goes through a stressful ordeal to get here, and now he is wondering if we would be willing to help him out!

"Mr. Jones, I will absolutely get ahold of Dr. Dasher. We'll get things moving quickly, but you will have to spend the night here receiving some IV fluids and antibiotics so tomorrow morning we can put you back together."

I will never forget this man's stoicism or perhaps just how different he is from so many other patients I've seen in the ER. He arrives with no fanfare or clamoring for help; he simply checks in and waits his turn to be seen. When neither the nurse nor I understand his story, he doesn't get huffy or angry. He just keeps trying to answer our questions the best way he can. This guy is straightforward; I like him. I should have been able to pick up on what he was trying to tell me.

I called Dr. Dasher, the surgeon, who came right in and was frightfully embarrassed at the breakdown of his earlier work. The next morning he took Mr. Jones to surgery to put everything back where it was supposed to be, and Mr. Jones went home uneventfully two days later.

❧ ❧ ❧

MR. JONES REMINDED ME of something I had overlooked but shouldn't have: figure out the patient's story—somehow, someway—using whatever means available. **Listen to comprehend; don't just hear words or go through the routine.** Ask real questions and wait for the answers. Never forget: it's all about understanding.

When I heard Mr. Jones's story, I missed the importance of what he was saying because he was not saying it in the way that I either wanted or expected. He was slow to speak, and when he finally did speak, his speech was too slow for me. Looking back, I realize that I became frustrated, and so I asked my questions with casual indifference. That indifference led to a predictable outcome: little insight into his situation. Ultimately, I failed to build a connection with him that could have helped me avoid my careless misdiagnosis. I was guilty of being a poor listener and was embarrassed that I needed to be reminded of this key ingredient of good medical care.

Mr. Jones taught me something else. I assumed he did not possess a worldly level of comfort with medical jargon and supposed he might erroneously describe hemorrhoids as guts. I was obviously wrong. **Assumptions can get a guy in trouble.**

His words, "That's what I've been trying to tell you," echo in my ears even now. More than a quarter of a century later, I still hear them. When I'm having trouble understanding what a patient is trying to tell me, I actively resist making an assumption that he doesn't know any better and can't speak medical jargon like I can. Jumping to a conclusion I think most logical is a crime I have committed more than once, and I would like to give up that habit. If I had given Mr. Jones a reasonable chance, I am pretty sure he would have been able to convey that his problem was located on his front side and not his back side; his lack of familiarity with hemorrhoids need not have been a critical issue. To this day I laugh at myself when I imagine the difference between a protruding half-inch hemorrhoid versus twelve feet of small intestine dangling from his belly.

I sure missed that diagnosis.

"Until I Die, Honor My Wishes"

BROKEN ENGLISH and multiple gestures were not enough to understand her story. I needed a delightful ten-year-old's assistance to appreciate all that had been happening to my newest emergency room patient, a petite, soft-spoken Hmong woman closing in on seventy years. Despite yeoman efforts, Shua Vang and I were unable to bridge the gap created by her sparse English and my inability to speak any of the Laotian language. This impasse guaranteed that her granddaughter, Xiong, would be a key player for the next hour.

As the three of us stuttered and stopped, I was struck by the quiet and unassuming dignity emanating from each and every syllable Shua spoke. Despite the intruding noises of a busy metropolitan hospital, room four became our private little world in which Shua talked, I listened, and Xiong translated. We toiled. I leaned toward Shua with each barely audible word. Frequent glances in Xiong's direction accompanied by a perplexed frown became the routine. I persevered in trying to understand and solve Shua Vang's puzzling abdominal pain. The background noises—cries of fear, pain-filled groans, and deep coughs—impeded progress as Shua stopped and waited for silence whenever a disruption intruded on our universe.

Communication was difficult and progress was slow, but finally we arrived at a point in time when words needed to be supplemented by a physical examination. I listened to her lungs. I checked her heart. I examined and reexamined her abdomen and pelvic region. I checked her organs multiple times with multiple techniques. I inspected her skin. I studied her eyes.

I didn't like my conclusions at all. The information Xiong had translated for me combined with my exam findings saddened me. I felt almost sick. Hallway distractions now seemed unduly loud and were grating on my nerves. I sensed an internal frustration; I was edgy because I knew what had to be done—I had to tell Shua and her family of my suspicions and recommendations. Tears and disbelief were inevitable. Awkward silences would be interrupted by stammering words and fractured sentences. I had traveled this road before, and it was never easy. Tonight especially, a sensitive heart-to-heart talk would be darn near impossible, what with the evolving carnival-like atmosphere invading our hectic ER.

My newest patient was sick—sicker than she knew. And I was tense. Conversations such as the one to come were gut-wrenching, and this one was destined to take place amid language hurdles, social barriers, and the unpredictable din coming from all parts of the emergency ward. I knew just how important it was for me to convey my impressions simply and without undue drama. Shua and her family would need to process what I shared. This would take awhile and couldn't be rushed.

But the luxury of time was not mine at the moment. Already my visit with Shua had been lengthy, and clamoring voices in the waiting area indicated a backlog of patients.

You've got to get moving, Scott—you're running way behind, and if an ambulance call comes in, you will be truly swamped.

Just then nine more members of Shua's family filed into the already cramped exam room, bringing the body count to an even dozen. I almost laughed at the prospect of trying to effectively communicate in that situation.

Taking a deep breath, I smiled at the youthful Xiong and said, "You've been a big help. Thank you so much."

The charming ten-year-old beamed, and her bashful grin spoke volumes. I turned to the gurney holding Shua. She was now completely encircled by her family. "Shua, you need to be in the hospital," I said gently, but my voice contained an urgency I had not intended.

And so it began. For the next twenty minutes the back-and-forth translations taxed our energies and frustrated our efforts to bridge the language barrier. The grinding process of listening, recapping, translating, speaking, and repeating the entire process over and over was obviously exhausting Xiong. The gravity of the messages magnified her challenge. But this wisp of a ten-year-old did her work. She helped all of us gain some understanding of the varying perspectives brought to the table. Still, this style of disjointed communication, albeit necessary, left me feeling alienated from the experience of Shua and her loved ones. The sounds of a language from the other side of the world were as gibberish to me, and I was confounded as to how just a few words from me could trigger three full minutes of chattering.

Good grief: I'm asking simple questions begging one-word responses. How much discussion does it take to say yes or no?

A tiny old man, wrinkled and solemn, finally stepped forward. Xiong introduced him as Shua's father, and she then presented Shua's husband, who inclined his head slightly in a show of respect. In the next few minutes I learned unforgettably that Shua's father, as family patriarch, was endowed with the ultimate decision-making responsibility. His declarations determined what would and would not happen. With a somber shake of his head he looked at me and turned to his great-granddaughter, slowly articulating some judiciously chosen and heartfelt words. He rasped out syllables I couldn't even begin to iterate, much less understand.

From Xiong, I heard, "No, Shua will come home. You do tests now and tell us later. We come back next week. You give Shua medicine—make her better."

I couldn't believe it! I wasn't prepared for this outright rejection of my recommendation, and I appealed to Shua with an emotional urgency, saying, "No, Shua, you are very sick. You need to be in the hospital! You really do."

Shua had to have understood my emotions, and she listened briefly as Xiong translated my plea. I squirmed. Watching seconds turn into minutes was unnerving, and I could feel my pulse quicken. Finally Shua looked at me and spoke, and I knew our visit was over. However her words were translated, her tone conveyed the simple and unmistakable message: "You are not in charge." A sense of hopelessness and letdown came over me, and I wondered how it was I hadn't been able to bridge the difference between Shua's perspective and mine. I had failed, and that was really all that mattered.

The gray, thinning locks in front of Shua's ears quietly slapped her cheekbones as she shook her head back and forth, prolonging the motion as if to reinforce Xiong's next words, which now spilled forth. "No, I go home. My father has decided. I take medicine you give me. I will come back when tests are done. Please, honor my wishes."

Xiong's words tumbled out in bunches, followed by disquieting intervals of silence. I was touched by the simplicity of Shua's last request: "Please, honor my wishes." I felt some shame that she even had to state such a concern.

My initial impression of Mrs. Shua Vang as a timid and quiet patient overwhelmed by the emergency room setting and likely amenable to my recommendations had been way off the mark. I was so wrong! After my unsuccessful effort to admit her to the hospital, Shua conferred with her family privately. I quickly attended to a couple more patients and returned to room four, where a formidable audience waited. Hoping for a change of heart from Shua and her father, I was again captivated by her casual and unassuming display of fortitude and resoluteness. A personal integrity ushered forth from the few words she spoke, and despite the fact that my medical opinion had been summarily dismissed, I was impressed by her resolve.

This family is guided by deep-rooted traditions that may frustrate me now but will sustain them in the days to come. I need to let go of my pride and do the best I can for Shua within the boundaries she and her family have set forth.

Shua was now surrounded by ten people who loved her without limit. They were mumbling and chattering away, sorting out options and plans and speaking with all the passion of a political convention. Worried faces and sparse words bespoke the gravity of this fearful hospital encounter; these folks were out of their element, and I felt for them. I wanted to reconnect with them and help them understand what was happening inside Shua's body. I wanted to bridge the obvious differences between us. I was almost embarrassed that "establishment" and "Western medicine" virtually oozed from my uniform, replete with scrubs and a white coat adorned with pockets filled with spiral-bound notebooks, stethoscope, reflex hammer, and pens. The gap between Shua's world and mine—the domain of scientific medicine versus the realm of herbs, spirituality, and natural remedies—seemed far too vast for a ten-year-old's words to bridge. My thoughts were at war.

You seriously need to get moving, Scott. You've got a house full of sick patients, and the nurses are giving you "the look"—telling you to put it in high gear. There is nothing more you can do here. Write some prescriptions and have Shua follow up next week with her family doc. You aren't going to get this ER emptied until after midnight, if then. And for the next two hours every patient you see will expect an apology for having to wait so long.

And so, finally, I gave up. I ordered some additional tests. Shua refused to wait for the results. On this crazy Friday night in the ER, with people scurrying here and there and the hubbub of voices everywhere, she had had enough and was going home. She wanted only some pills to make her feel better. I wrote prescriptions to reduce stomach acid and gave follow-up instructions for her to see Dr. Wells the next week.

After completing checkout procedures, Shua and her family trundled toward the exit. I stood twenty feet away and watched them leave. I was concerned for her and pretty sure her symptoms would accelerate; complications were probably right around the corner.

Oh, well. I tried my best, but she's the one in charge.

Patients should realize that few physicians approach living wills with the same resolve they bring to a surgical problem or a medical crisis.

With a disappointing sense of resignation, as I pivoted toward the chart rack to prepare for my next patient, I heard a loud belch followed by a low groan and then the easily recognized sounds of retching. I turned back to see Shua gag and stumble, spewing bloody red vomitus throughout most of the waiting area. Other patients shrieked and dodged, not interested in colliding with Shua's last meal. But as quickly as it started, it ended. The eerie silence was interrupted only by Shua's muffled weeping and her husband's prayer-like utterances. The waiting room was a mess, filled with a stench not soon forgotten.

I asked a nearby nurse, "Please put her back in room four," and I then proceeded to reexamine Shua. Her abdomen was far more tender than it had been just an hour earlier. I was convinced her internal bleeding came from her stomach or small intestine. Sadly, I looked at Shua and told Xiong to ask her if she would let me admit her to the hospital. Xiong and Shua conversed, and Shua grudgingly nodded her head, quietly sobbing. I gently touched her hand, trying to erase any shame or embarrassment resulting from the horrific waiting room scene.

Unbeknownst to Shua or me, this was the beginning of the end.

Over the next forty-eight hours, I evaluated Shua with a multitude of blood, urine, stool, and imaging tests. Unfortunately, she had cancer of the stomach—the blood and vomitus and pain were the products of a cruel tumor mass burrowing a crater that perforated her stomach lining. She lost a lot of blood, and multiple transfusions were necessary. Even worse, the demon had already spread to regions both above and below her diaphragm, signifying "the horse was out of the barn." Her cancer would be relentless and would likely allow only a few months of life.

Prior to the emergency room drama, I had never met Shua, but she occupied much of my weekend thinking. On Monday morning I turned her care over to her family physician, Dr. Jim Wells, and summarized what had happened over the weekend. I suggested a cancer specialist be consulted and a living will document be completed.

Four days later, physicians going off call were transferring responsibility for their patients to me since I was the on-call doctor for the weekend. When it was Dr. Wells's turn, he told me that Shua was reasonably stable but doing poorly in terms of eating or drinking, and then he dropped a bombshell.

"Dr. Jensen, I didn't get a living will done. I'll meet with Shua and an interpreter next week if things have settled down by then. This has been a tough week for the entire family, and it seemed premature to race ahead and start talking about final wishes. I don't think she's ready for that quite yet."

Whoa! How did he come up with that? Shua and her family will definitely want to direct the plans and interventions scheduled during her hospitalization and future care.

"Dr. Wells, I couldn't disagree with you more. I admitted Shua to the hospital last weekend, and we had a minor disaster in the ER waiting room. I told you that on Monday. This family has a strong sense of what they want done and how they want it done, and I'm pretty sure they are going to want to direct how things unfold over the next few weeks. I'm disappointed you didn't even give her a chance to sign a Do Not Resuscitate form, because I think she will emphatically decline any heroic efforts."

"Well," Dr. Wells responded hesitatingly, almost apologetically, "it won't be an easy discussion, what with the language barrier and everything. And it's not as if I have a long-standing relationship with her. I've known her for less than a year. I wanted to wait for things to settle down just a bit, and maybe talk about it at a follow-up visit in the clinic . . . you know . . . once we get her discharged and plugged into a chemotherapy program. I think it'll go easier then."

"Jim, what are you talking about?" I replied with exasperation. "Shua and her family have already demonstrated that they will decide what interventions will occur, and I doubt they are going to consent to any chemo drugs. A living will is probably the most important thing we can do for her. Her prognosis is dismal. If CPR or any heroic measures were implemented against her will, that would be a shame. You had a week to address this issue, and interpreter services have been available."

"Let's not get too excited" was Dr. Wells's rejoinder.

"Good grief," I spluttered, "in her fragile condition, she could die this weekend!"

Because death at some not-too-distant point was virtually inevitable due to her advanced cancer, I did not want to have to call on a ten-year-old granddaughter to handle the delicate task of determining what support or interventions Shua would want. I pursed my lips to avoid saying anything more. Dr. Wells understood my frustration with his avoidance of having the "hard talk," and it was obvious that our relationship had been wounded—deeply. No more words were necessary.

After an uncomfortable silence, Dr. Wells assured me that Shua would have the opportunity to meet with an interpreter and declare her living will instructions in the following week.

I watched Shua like a hawk for the next three days, and she survived the weekend.

A living will was completed.

A month went by and on a chilly autumn day her spirit left us, but our memory of her did not.

૪ ૪ ૪

A CRITICAL REMINDER EMERGES for both patient and doctor: regardless of how awkward an end-of-life discussion might be, this fact does not alter the necessity of promptly giving the "hard talk" its due. Shua was temporarily denied the opportunity to direct the scope of her care because of physician procrastination and apprehension. Patients should realize that few physicians approach living wills with the same resolve they bring to a surgical problem or a medical crisis. **In this day and age, patients need to be far more than passive followers regarding life-and-death issues.** They deserve the chance to direct their care, and assertiveness may be necessary. Interestingly, it is often the nurses who save the day by initiating the "hard talk" with patients and families.

Shua, dignified and strong, caused me to reflect long and hard about the difficulty for patients to take charge of their care in the midst of intimidating doctors, unfamiliar jargon, and death lurking just around the corner. I often wondered what Shua might have said to me had I been present during her final moments of consciousness. I have a suspicion that through Xiong, my ten-year-old assistant, Shua would have issued this instruction: **"Until I die, honor my wishes."**

Recognition
and
CELEBRATION

Recognition and celebration honor achievement,

but even more provide a reminder:

"To whom much is given,

much is expected."

"Doctor, Are You Happy with Your Job?"

"Dr. Jensen, can I ask you something?"

"Go ahead, Stan."

There is no way I can refuse Stan the opportunity to ask me anything he wants. He is a gem: ninety-two years old and still driving tractor, rain or shine, ten hours at a time, planting corn to help his son with the family farm. His list of medical issues reads like an encyclopedia: coronary artery bypass of four vessels, stroke with a facial droop, heart attack, high blood pressure, hearing loss requiring hearing aids, anemia, and severe kidney failure.

Stan is an old-fashioned contributor, and America needs more people like him. He just retired from the local church council after twenty-some years because—as he said—"my hearing's so bad, I didn't think it's fair to make everybody holler at a church meeting."

"Doc, I read a magazine last month that reported on a survey of doctors who were asked if they were happy with their job. Do you know what the results showed?"

I shook my head.

"The article stated that many doctors aren't happy with their jobs and look forward to retirement as soon as possible. The most common reasons given for their job dissatisfaction were excessive criticism of care and fear of being sued. Here's my question for you: are you happy with your job?"

"Stan, I'm one of the luckiest guys I know. I love my job."

A lopsided grin appeared on his face and grew into a beaming smile. He chuckled. "I sort of thought you might say something like that. You always seem to be in a good mood, and you act like you're happy to see us."

"Stan, I like my patients, and I am happy to see them. It's my privilege to be involved in their care. Over time many become friends. I've got the best job in the world. I get to take care of people like you; I learn every day; I work in a building that's warm in the winter and cool in the summer. There are days I go home knowing absolutely that I got to contribute to God's earthly plan—that feels good."

Interesting. This discussion reminds me how fortunate I am to do the work I do. Stan's concern regarding my welfare is renewing.

Stan interrupted my pleasant reverie by saying, "But the survey indicated most doctors don't feel the way you do. Why do you think that is?"

"Stan, I'll let you in on a little secret. Doctors actually have pretty thin skin even though we're respected and do important work. When patients are critical of our efforts or insurance companies tell us that we have to do things differently, we struggle—in part because we worked so hard and long learning how to be a doctor. We tend to take things too personally. I remember getting sued twenty-five years ago, and I didn't handle it very well. I saw a patient once and did my best. I went along with her request, but told her I didn't think it was the best approach. She ignored my recommendations, and when things turned sour, she hired a lawyer. It didn't seem to matter to her that I had advised against her plan. She sued me, and it hurt. The case was settled out of court, but I'll never forget how it affected me. I felt wounded and exposed. I remember having paranoid thoughts such as, *Everybody thinks I goofed up and I'm a lousy doctor.* Looking back I know I should have dealt with it better. So like I said, doctors can be pretty sensitive to disapproval."

Stan asked, "Do you think there is anything a patient can do to help his doctor be happier?"

"Sure—just be like you, Stan!"

He couldn't contain his laughter.

"All kidding aside, I mean what I said, Stan. You've always been appreciative, and you understand there are no guarantees in life. You thank me for my efforts and take an interest in me as a person. Doctors enjoy positive feedback as well as the occasional expression of gratitude. We're no different than anyone else; our socks go on one at a time."

Stan seemed intrigued by our discussion, so I continued.

"Thirty years ago, psychologists described a pattern of behavior that fits many doctors. It was called the 'imposter syndrome,' characterized by high-achieving people who harbor a subconscious fear that they aren't as smart or talented as other people think they are. They feel a need to always do more and do it better. They can't stomach the idea of being 'found out' as 'not so great.' Being seen as average is hazardous to their mental and emotional health. The question, 'What have I done lately?' relentlessly pursues them. I know the imposter syndrome fits me. I constantly push myself. I don't know why I am the way I am, but sometimes I feel as though I'm addicted to new challenges because achievement satisfies the 'fix' I need to reassure myself that I've done something worthwhile lately."

"You sure are on the go all the time, Doc. Nobody can miss that."

"Stan, being both thin-skinned and determined to excel makes it difficult for doctors to be at ease, and this is where a patient can really make a difference. If things don't go as planned and a patient of mine suffers, it's tough on me. But if that patient tells me, 'Doc, I know you did your best, and it didn't work out quite the way we wanted, but thanks for helping out and trying,' I am reinvigorated to keep doing my best.

Doctors can exhibit some pretty strange behaviors.

Instead of licking my wounds, I can move on to my next patient and let go of the disappointing outcome. Patients do influence doctors' behavior—more than they know. Quite honestly, Stan, you make me want to be the best doctor I can be."

⁄◎ ⁄◎ ⁄◎

OUR DISCUSSION REMINDED ME of a former colleague who had a tendency to suggest to his patients they were seeing him "in the nick of time," implying that any further delay may have resulted in their demise. He was shameless in this self-promotion, causing me to wonder why such a highly skilled physician needed that kind of self-administered pat on the back. Evidently being a doctor wasn't quite enough to satisfy his need for accomplishment or status, so he overcame the imposter syndrome by proclaiming himself to be a Rambo figure saving the day with no time to spare.

Doctors can exhibit some pretty strange behaviors.

⁄◎ ⁄◎ ⁄◎

PATIENTS AND PHYSICIANS need one another. They support one another. **The value of a physician's service to a patient is usually plain to see, but the reciprocal gift from a patient—a renewing force that sustains a physician's commitment to healing—is easily overlooked.** Health care reform over the last quarter century has deeply intruded into the manner of caring for the sick and suffering, and it is not uncommon for "doctoring" to feel like "factory work." When that happens, "burnout" is just around the corner, and the best remedy for that is the rejuvenating energy a patient can give.

Stan's encouragement through the years provided me with many gifts, but none more important than these: enthusiasm for the morning, engagement through the day, and satisfaction in the evening.

DOCTORS ENJOY POSITIVE FEEDBACK

AS WELL AS THE OCCASIONAL

EXPRESSION OF GRATITUDE.

WE'RE NO DIFFERENT THAN ANYONE ELSE;

OUR SOCKS GO ON ONE AT A TIME.

Embrace
the Attitude;
Gain
the Latitude

Henry was a delightful ninety-six-year-old man who enjoyed telling me slightly off-color jokes about sex in the senior population, and he derived special satisfaction from doing so in front of his sixty-year-old daughter. Perhaps he even enjoyed it a little too much. She would turn red and look at the ceiling while he chuckled at her sullied modesty, thoroughly enjoying his violation of good manners. Their connection was warm and comfortable and fun to watch. It was a pleasure to be involved in his care, and I found it intriguing that his humorous tales frequently opened a door into more worrisome concerns that he otherwise might not have mentioned.

On a spring day in May he asked me about a friend of his in the assisted living center. "Doc, why do you think Ed would want to marry an eighty-nine-year-old gal? I mean, what's the point? He's ninety years old, and it's not as if they're going to move into a house or anything. I still can't get over it. Their wedding is this Saturday, and I haven't been able to change his mind. Lord knows, I've tried."

Better wait on answering, Scott: this looks like a no-win situation. Say nothing and see what develops.

After enduring my silence for too long, Henry finally blurted, "So you don't have any better idea than I do why Ed's getting married. Can you believe it? At his age, he's going to tie the knot."

"Well, Henry, love is a funny thing," I said with a smile.

"Humph," Henry grunted.

The room was quiet, and Henry's daughter furrowed her brow. She didn't understand why Henry was so bothered about Ed's decision to participate in matrimony, and neither did I.

"Oh, by the way, if he—Ed, that is—needs to," Henry stammered, "could he—ahhh—try the blue pill? If things go in that direction, I mean."

I think I'm beginning to see what Henry is up to. This may be a chance to even the score for all the times he has embarrassed his daughter and me.

"You know what I mean, Doc. I mean if he can't . . . perform."

I grinned at his reference to the pill's color instead of saying its name. "Sure, Henry, a ninety-year-old man can use Viagra if he needs it and wants to give it a try, but that's presuming his medical situation doesn't disqualify him from its use. I don't know anything about Ed's health since I've never met him, but I'm confused by your interest in his sex life. What's up? Did you guys talk about this? Did he want you to check it out with me? I probably know his doctor. I could call him and have him get in touch with Ed."

"Oh, ahhh, no, no, don't do that," Henry sputtered nervously. "He didn't ask me. We didn't talk about it. But, okay, well . . . I just thought I might pass along any information you gave me. You know, Doc, Ed and I are pretty good friends and we talk a lot, so I figured I would just do some checking on this blue pill. Obviously it's up to him, but I thought if he's going to the trouble of getting married at his age, he might as well give it a try."

After a lengthy pause, I looked straight at Henry and raised an eyebrow, saying, "Now you know, Henry, that because of the medications you take, your situation is different. You can't use Viagra because you take nitrate pills every day. The combination of nitrates and Viagra can be lethal."

I feel like I'm watching that old Jack Nicholson movie. A patient is having a heart attack, and to save face with his girlfriend, he lies about using Viagra. Just as the doctor is about to inject nitrates into his vein, the patient blurts out that he took a dose of Viagra an hour earlier. He is mortified because not only did his girlfriend gain an understanding of what was on his mind, but the fact of his "compromised manhood" was now out in the open.

Henry was torn regarding a response. He may have wanted to deny any personal interest, but he knew this would sound false, and an outright confession that his interest in the blue pill was not really about Ed would be too embarrassing. My words had been presented as mere information, but still I had called his bluff—and he realized it. For once, he was the one who blushed.

This is sort of fun.

He finally burst out, "Oh, Doc, don't worry about me. I don't need those pills. I mean—what I mean is—that I wouldn't be asking for any blue pills because my girlfriend and I, ahhh, we aren't interested in that kind of stuff."

Henry's daughter was six feet away, and her face was reddening. She had just heard far more than she wanted: her father likely suffered from erectile dysfunction, and he had a girlfriend with whom he might have a sexual interest. Daughters seldom want to hear this kind of talk.

As for Henry, a little discomfiture wouldn't be the end of the world, and he deserved it, if for no other reason than he routinely dished it out and watched others squirm. His ploy to use Ed's upcoming wedding as a way to broach his own questions about Viagra had backfired.

... an outright confession about his interest in the blue pill would be too embarrassing.

I love that the attraction between men and women isn't extinguished with old age. The flame may falter, but it takes precious little to fan smoldering embers back to life.

Even though Henry's pride may have taken a hit, a valuable lesson for patients and doctors presented itself: the bond we shared allowed Henry to address topics that might otherwise have been avoided. This day it was Viagra, but another day it might be a fear of dying or the pain of living or the misery of dementia.

*These are the moments that keep me from feeling as though I'm getting on a treadmill in the morning. My patients invigorate me with their gifts: humor, poignancy, and the invitation to simply be me. Today Henry has taught me something very valuable regarding patients: **if I can embrace their attitude, I am given the latitude** to go where I might otherwise not be welcome.*

As I closed his chart and got up to leave, Henry reached out and put his hand on mine. "Doc, I'm pretty lucky. I can trust you, and at my age not a whole lot else matters."

"Thanks, Henry, but the privilege is all mine."

❧ ❧ ❧

TWENTY MINUTES after I had been caring for a man just shy of the century mark, here was a gurgling bundle of joy at the opposite end of the life spectrum. I have never been one to think that newborns are particularly cute, but this two-month-old really was beautiful. Curly blonde hair, big blue eyes, and pouting pink lips created a striking appearance for this pretty baby girl.

It is so wonderful being a family doc, blessed by patients who brighten my day with gifts of fun and thankfulness and the occasional life lesson. What could be better?

Sarah was receiving her first vaccinations, and her parents were nervous. Their desire to make perfect decisions for their precious angel was obvious, and their fear of not knowing how she would react to the shots had them frenzied. In fact, so relentless were their questions that finally I held up my hands, signaling for a time-out.

"Listen, folks, in the years to come you are going to sacrifice so much for this delightful little girl and work so hard on her behalf that I need to tell you something: it just isn't possible to make perfect decisions. You will make countless good decisions for Sarah's sake, and yet you will second-guess yourselves to the point of obsession. But because your choices will be based on love and a willingness to sacrifice time, money, sleep, and whatever else it takes to do right by her, it'll work out. All you can do is your best, and because you love Sarah so much, your decisions will be good enough."

My relationship with these young parents was solidified that morning, and I could see their apprehension melt away. By embracing and sharing their attitude of sheer joy for their child, I was granted the latitude to counsel them to let go of their desire to make perfect choices. **Their decisions would be based on love, and this had to be enough.**

Sarah barely whimpered when the nurse administered the vaccines.

⁂

"GO AHEAD, JASON: tell Dr. Jensen what you told me when I was recovering from my surgery."

Jason's face broke into the best smile in the whole world. He was a forty-year-old mentally challenged man-child who lived with his sixty-year-old mom and loved her desperately.

"Shucks, Dr. Jensen, I just told Mom that I might have to move out: too much drama with all her surgeries."

The three of us broke into boisterous laughter at the ridiculousness of Jason's threat. He and his mother loved each other with a bond that would never allow any earthly parting. Two years earlier his dad had died at the hands of a mean-spirited melanoma cancer, leaving Trudy and Jason to figure out how they would navigate their earthly journey together.

Since then, Jason had joyfully broadcast his commitment to protect and support his mom; his resolve was stunning and heartwarming. His cognitive skills may have been limited, but God had gifted Jason with an ability to exhibit such sweet fondness and unconditional caring that it caused others to step back and reexamine their own capacity to do what Jason did so naturally—love without inhibition and demand nothing in return.

During the topsy-turvy time of Trudy's surgeries and convalescence, Jason blossomed, and his teasing comment about moving out was precious. Jason may have been absolutely dependent on his mother for food and shelter, but his daily testimony that life could be lovely and authentic was a reciprocal gift to Trudy worth more than gold.

Embracing Jason's attitude that morning gave me pause to examine my own life with all of its hiccups and hassles and helped me better appreciate that **the interruptions of my day had no more authority over my life than what I allowed.**

⁂

THREE WONDERFUL PATIENT VISITS took place in a span of two hours on that memorable morning. I was poignantly reminded of the privilege of being invited into their very special worlds.

That blessing-filled day brought to mind thankfulness and respect for the patient-physician connection. These patients touched my spirit with a renewing energy and taught me something important about building relationships: **embrace the attitude, gain the latitude, and a powerful bond may grow.**

"It Is in Giving That We Receive"

Make me an instrument of your peace . . .
Oh Divine Master,
grant that I may, not so much seek
to be consoled as to console;
to be understood as to understand;
to be loved as to love;
for it is in giving that we receive,
it is in pardoning that we are pardoned, and
it is in dying that we are born to eternal life.
St. Francis of Assisi

Lofty-sounding phrases, easily recited, incredibly difficult to live by, and yet I was to witness this poem in action—a gift beyond measure.

🐟 🐟 🐟

My fingers were numb from the cold wind, and gloves would have been nice. November was supposed to be a prelude to winter, not the real deal. But this Thursday was frigid and blustery, with all the makings of a bone-chilling January deep freeze. The lack of sunshine worsened my already dreary mood, and I felt smothered by melancholy.

Being mired in sadness wasn't typical for me, but I knew the reason and told myself "it is what it is" (my usual self-talk when encountering unchangeable circumstances). As I trudged up the steps to the front door, I reflected that sometimes house calls can be uplifting experiences, opportunities to see patients celebrate real progress—perhaps recuperating from a joint replacement or getting a new lease on life following a heart valve replacement. But I knew this trip would contain no merriment. Today my much-loved patient and I would engage in an awkward dance avoiding the obvious; we would sidestep a confrontation with the inevitable gut-wrenching outcome.

Mary Kay knew her days were limited. She'd had a splendid run. Despite the original depressing prognosis of three months to live, she had defied the experts, living with gusto and passionately pursuing adventures for more than three years.

The last few weeks had been painful to watch as the lifeblood of this delightful forty-year-old woman trickled away. She was aware that the end was just around the corner. Everybody around her recognized the brutal reality of the matter. The angel of death was growing impatient. Dismally, I accepted the sad reality that I could only watch and wait, like everybody else. I was supposed to be more capable; I was supposed to be more useful. I did not feel capable, nor did I feel useful.

Nature is so harsh. Life moves forward, time ticks by, the dead are buried. Cancer is a mean-spirited demon. Mary Kay is filled with the cells of this monster, and she no longer has the strength to fight back. This tumor with its single-minded aim—consume the host until death arrives—is even now ravaging the few pounds of flesh Mary Kay has been able to hold on to.

"How're you doing today, Mary Kay?"

"Not so bad, Dr. Jensen. Things are happening—you told me they would. I'm getting weaker, but I'm not uncomfortable. Sleep would be nice—I mean deep sleep so I could feel refreshed and want to actually do something, anything. Having my hair washed is exhausting, so I skipped it the last two days."

"Are you having any pain?"

"Not enough to complain about, and I'm glad for that."

A few more questions and a brief exam revealed no surprises. She was—as much as possible—content with her situation. She did not need or want me to dispense some sort of false hope to soothe her psyche. Somehow she realized excess or unwarranted hope might distort her ability to see what was really happening. While she appreciated that reassurances might be helpful for what must be endured, she had no interest in dying with blinders on. False hope could threaten her very strong intention to have her end-of-life care be focused on pain control, preservation of dignity, and helping her family in the grieving process.

"By the way, thanks for coming to see me," she murmured as she drifted off for a few moments.

The narcotics are doing their job. I'm glad she's been taking some the last couple of weeks. She's been pretty stubborn, wanting to use no more pain meds than absolutely necessary because she cherishes a clear head when she has visitors. For such a delicate person, I'm surprised at her willingness to bear as much pain as she does.

For more than three years, Mary Kay had lived a dual existence, with cancer and chemotherapy always present, only to be pushed aside by her zeal to live fully. Her final months would not be described by a doomsday attitude waiting around for the fulfillment of a lousy prognosis. She refused to live life waiting for storms to pass; instead she simply chose to dance in the rain. Her go-for-it attitude was contagious, and her spirit was a reminder to seize the day and live with gusto. Her witness to living well rather than living long would be a lasting legacy.

Her eyes fluttered open, and she said, "Why are you still here, Dr. Scott? You should get a life!" And she chuckled quietly at her brazen declaration.

I smiled and said, "I'll be on my way soon enough. I'm headed to the office. I taught at the medical school this morning and just wanted to stop by and make sure you were doing okay."

"Humph," she said, then continued, "What's up with you today? Something's going on. You seem a little gloomy, almost sad. That's not like you."

"Nothing's going on," I protested, feeling some shame at having a dying person attend to my transparent mood.

She spoke with a haunting softness. "Scott, just because I'm dying doesn't mean I'm stupid. You really do seem down. What's going on?"

I blurted, "Good grief, Mary Kay, you don't need to hear about my problems. It's nothing."

"Honestly, I would really like to hear what's going on. Everyone seems to think I'm made of glass. I'm not that fragile. Tell me what's happening. Please."

Her convincing plea broke down my resistance, and I confessed, "Well, I've decided to leave the clinic I've been at for the last fifteen years. I'm going to interview for a full-time teaching job at the medical school. It's a big change. I guess I'm trying to get my arms around what it'll be like leaving my patients."

"Whew, that is a big decision! Your life will change a lot. What made you decide that?"

"I don't exactly know. I'm not sure how it came about. I don't even know when I actually decided. But I know these days at the clinic, I feel like a square peg trying to fit in a round hole, and it's time for me to make a change."

"Hmmm. You leaving private practice surprises me, Doc, it really does."

Perplexed, I said, "Why's that?"

"Your decision to quit seeing patients, one on one, doesn't sit right with me. I think that's what you're meant to do. You're good at it, and patients like knowing you're at their side. I'm sorry for sticking my nose in your business, but I really think you should be involved with patients, up front and personal, like you have been with me. It's who you are, and it's what you do."

"Well, I feel like I'm burning out. My enthusiasm for going to the clinic is gone. The office feels like a treadmill, and that's not where I want to be."

Mary Kay thought for a while and then said, "Okay, I get that, but what I'm hearing you say is that you're frustrated with the place you're at, not with taking care of people. Am I misunderstanding?"

Hmmm. My enjoyment of caring for patients hasn't really changed. I suppose the real issue is the workplace.

"No, Mary Kay, you heard me correctly: taking care of patients is still a passion for me. You make a good point: I suppose the real problem is where I work, not the work I do. Our clinic used to be like family, but we grew a lot, and we changed. We're now a full-fledged corporation complete with bureaucracy, policy manuals, rules, and red tape. I'm sure some of it has to do with all the government and big-business influences; it probably couldn't be helped. Anyway, somewhere along the line, and I don't really know when, I realized I didn't belong anymore. I know I've changed, too, so it's not like it's the clinic's fault. Things just aren't the same. From my perspective, hassles and frustration are on the rise and happiness is on the decline."

"Yeah, well, then I can see why you're troubled. But your passion for your patients is still there—I can sense it. I remember our lunch three years ago when Mom and Dad asked if you would take over my care. I mean, we were all so scared and getting no answers; all we knew was that I had a softball-sized tumor in my belly and a whole lot of blood in my urine. You listened so intently, I wondered if you were hard of hearing, and then you fired off about ten point-blank questions. After you heard the answers, you said you would do it—you would be my doctor. Two days later you called me with a plan for completing the work-up, and the whirlwind began. Do you remember that?"

"Oh yeah, I sure do. The specialists we contacted at UCLA were terrific. I remember when you had the big surgery, and then ultimately they reinjected your own revved-up cells back into you. It was a wild ride."

"Yeah, well, it was a good ride, and I'm grateful. A three-month death sentence turned into more than three years of good living and a lot of terrific times. I appreciate that so much, more than you can know. But getting back to you, I'm sure you'd be good at teaching, but I think you're called to be there for people like you have been for me. Leaving your current workplace doesn't bother me, but leaving the world of one-on-one caring for patients—I don't think that's the right move. Seeing patients and helping them in a very personal way—that fulfills you. It's your strong suit."

In that moment everything changed. The room was quiet. Mary Kay had exhausted herself by lecturing me. And I was surprised, confused, and even a bit riled by her bluntness.

We wrapped up our business. Both of us satisfied our inner need to extend loving wishes to each other. We knew this might be our last meeting, so we both took care to address that painful reality. Then I left.

I sat in my car, dazed.

What the heck just happened in there?

I thought a long time, and by the time I drove away, I had come to realize that the trajectory of my career had been altered dramatically. Mary Kay had accomplished a remarkable feat: she had changed me. She had redirected my course by challenging me with words filled with naked and raw simplicity: "Seeing patients and helping them in a very personal way—that fulfills you. It's your strong suit."

The next morning I canceled the upcoming interview at the medical school.

"From my perspective, hassles and frustration are on the rise and happiness is on the decline."

ⱥ ⱥ ⱥ

A THURSDAY AFTERNOON house call designed to attend the sick and the dying morphed into the birth of Catalyst Medical Clinic. The subsequent demands of starting a clinic were at times overwhelming, but the journey was worth every waking hour, and to this day I consider Mary Kay to be the true catalyst of a new beginning in my service to patients.

I had no idea just how much I needed Mary Kay that day. Although my intention had been to attend to her concerns, she reversed our roles, and it changed my life and career. The words of St. Francis, **"it is in giving that we receive,"** took on new meaning for me when my desire to give comfort came full circle and instead I received comfort from her. Whatever I might have given her that day was paltry in comparison to the gift I had received—an insight both powerful and heartfelt.

A week later Mary Kay died. A tumor the size of a grapefruit had used her kidney as an inroad from which it traveled to all points on the compass. It did what it does best—it destroyed her body. But it never gained the satisfaction of extinguishing her spirit. The cancer may have poisoned her kidneys and taken her earthly life, but it never touched her indomitable soul.

≈ ≈ ≈

Patients, never forget this: doctors need you, in ways you cannot know, in ways you could not guess. You are a critical ingredient for our professional growth, but more importantly you also renew our spirit to heal, which is the heart and soul of a career in medicine.

Daily we listen to complaints and woes and try to muster the compassion and energy to be the caregivers we might be. Without you, we are nothing more than chemistry and biology whiz kids with some distinctive letters behind our names. With your touch, we begin to comprehend the words in the oath that has guided doctors for thousands of years: **I will remember that there is art to medicine as well as science, and that warmth, sympathy, and understanding may outweigh the surgeon's knife or the chemist's drug** (excerpt of the modern version of Hippocratic Oath by Louis Lasagna, Tufts University, 1964).

On a day in which the clouds hid the sun, the touch of a saint brightened my soul and rejuvenated my calling, and I saw firsthand the power of these words: **in weakness is strength.**

PATIENTS SHOULD NEVER FORGET THIS—

doctors need you.

PHYSICIANS NEED TO REMEMBER

there is art to medicine as well as science;

warmth, sympathy, and understanding

may outweigh the surgeon's knife

or the chemist's drug.

A Snake
with
Pneumonia

"So, how was your first night on call?" asked my wife, Mary, aware that I had just been baptized into the world of covering call duties for the intensive care unit.

"You wouldn't believe it. It was incredible! An elderly man had a heart attack, and then his heart stopped. I called a code blue, and the staff initiated CPR with chest compressions. Then I had to shock him, and . . . he came back to us! I mean, there he was, talking and even smiling after it looked like he was dead. I was so excited for him. The nurses were terrific; they helped me through the entire process of resuscitation, giving me suggestions and stepping in to do whatever was necessary."

"That's amazing. What a night!" she exclaimed.

"And that's not all! Four more times during the night his heart stopped, and each time we resuscitated him successfully. Five times in one night I had to put the shock paddles to his chest to restart his heart. But when my shift was over, there was this nice old man from Latvia, still alive and breathing, chatting with his wife as though nothing special had happened."

Leaning into

their knowledge

and experience

helped me

develop the

skills I needed

to become

a proficient

physician.

Mary nodded approvingly. "Nice job! That's a heck of a first call night."

"Yeah, it was. Thanks. By the way, how was your day yesterday at the clinic?"

Mary had an interesting job as a veterinarian. She worked with a lot of exotic animals, including birds, hamsters, iguanas, and snakes along with the more routine dog and cat appointments.

"Well, let's see. I guess I did see an interesting client yesterday."

"Tell me what happened," I said.

"A boa constrictor came in, and he was pretty good sized—probably six-feet long with a hefty girth. Anyway, he had pneumonia, so that was sort of interesting."

I scoffed at the notion that my wife had treated a boa constrictor for pneumonia and wisecracked, "Oh, really? And just how did you treat this noble creature of the earth? Did you give him a shot of penicillin?"

She smiled demurely and nodded. "Yes, I did. How did you know?"

It took a few moments for that to sink in. Mary proceeded to fill in some details about the snake having a runny nose and what his lungs sounded like. She had indeed given him a shot of penicillin. She went on to tell me how snakes have only one functioning lung, and when she used her stethoscope to listen to the boa constrictor's respirations, the sounds were consistent with pneumonia, just like she might hear in a dog or a cat.

I threw up my hands and laughed. "Good grief! Five times in one night a man is shocked back to life, and that's not enough to match your story about a boa constrictor with pneumonia. I give up!"

❧ ❧ ❧

THE GENTLEMAN FROM LATVIA provided me with a profound confidence-building experience. On follow-up rounds I monitored his progress, and he was sent home a few days later with a brand-new pacemaker in place. I was pleased for him and thankful for the chance to be a part of his ongoing story.

But I was also immensely grateful to have learned a powerful lesson on my very first night of critical care call: **The value of developing strong working relationships with the nursing staff could not be overstated. Leaning into their knowledge and experience helped me develop the skills and know-how I needed to become a proficient physician.** Without the nurses, my Latvian patient might have left the hospital in a body bag. In the first days of my internship I had had the good fortune to realize that I would learn more and err less if I partnered with seasoned staff and dedicated mentors.

But, of course, I also learned that if I think I've seen something so special its uniqueness could not be outdone, I better check to see if my wife is around. Her tales of exotic animals and their adventurous needs can be so bizarre that human medicine seems tame by comparison.

PATIENTS CAN BE
so PRECIOUS

"Doctor, why was I transferred to the hospital when I was at the nursing home?"

I was clueless and mystified by her question, so I asked, "What are you talking about, Celia?"

"You know, when I had my hip replaced I was at the nursing home recovering, and then suddenly I was being whisked away to the hospital by ambulance."

"Celia, I don't remember that. When was your hip replaced? About how long ago was that?"

"Oh, let's see now. It must have been all of six years ago, maybe longer."

Good grief, out of the blue she expects me to remember that? Oh well, I better follow up on her concern because who knows where this will lead.

"I'm sorry, Celia. I don't recall anything about that transfer. That was a long time ago."

"Oh, I see. I was just sort of wondering."

Hmmm, something is up. Don't ignore her question.

"Do you want me to look in your chart to see what I can find?"

"Well, if you have the time," she replied, adding, "It's sort of been on my mind."

And so I did. I quickly thumbed through fifty pages of old reports and found what I was looking for. It had been more than eight years ago: she had developed a bladder infection in the nursing home while recovering from her hip replacement, and the sudden onset of a high fever had prompted a rapid trip to the hospital via ambulance. She had stayed two days for intravenous fluids and antibiotics and was discharged back to the nursing home for more physical therapy. The next two weeks in the nursing home were uneventful, and she was discharged back to her own home, where she has been living since and doing very well. She does her own cleaning, cooking, shoveling, and yard care; she plays cards every week with some lady friends and drives around town in all sorts of weather. Her ninetieth birthday is not far off.

"I have the hospital report here, Celia. You developed a bladder infection and had to go to the hospital by ambulance because you had a high fever."

"That's right! I remember now."

A long pause ensued, and I was perplexed about this conversation and where it was headed.

"I remember that ambulance ride pretty well, Doctor."

I had no idea what to say or add, so I said nothing.

Celia looked at me and sheepishly smiled. I sensed she was having some difficulty deciding just how to say whatever it was she wanted to tell me. Her words suddenly spilled out. "The paramedic who took care of me on the way to the hospital was, ah, well . . . He sure could put his shoes under my bed," she said conspiratorially.

I was initially dumbfounded, and then the meaning of her words finally dawned on me. "So he was pretty good looking, huh, Celia?"

She smiled and nodded coyly. "The driver wasn't bad to look at either. I don't quite know why I remember that ride so well, but I sure do."

I smiled broadly and reflected that it was pretty darned special for this lady to share her vivid memories from nearly a decade ago. Being practically eighty years old at the time and being rushed to the hospital didn't stop her from recognizing a handsome young man, and she obviously wanted to share this little secret with me. I felt privileged to hear it, and I was a little flabbergasted to think that her earlier questions prompting me to review eight years of medical notes were designed to help her get to her confession.

Hmmm, so in the 1920s when Celia was a young woman, the words "he sure could put his shoes under my bed" signified interest. Pretty funny.

I said a silent prayer of thanks for the intriguing chemistry our Creator instilled into men and women. **The magical enchantment humans hold for one another is certainly not age dependent.**

Patients can be so precious. Celia, with her confession of long-ago memories about a handsome paramedic, makes me smile. Her curious choice of words— "he sure could put his shoes under my bed"—reminds me of another patient: tiny Thelma, an eighty-eight-year-old lady who occasionally uses a mystifying word or phrase, resulting in an amusing interpretation. (She also has a peculiar habit of patting my thigh before she asks a question.)

Thelma is legendary in our clinic for her unique and sometimes misleading terminology. A few months ago, Thelma leaned close to me, patted my thigh (pretty high up), and said, "Dr. Jensen, I've been thinking about getting a living will, and I have a question."

She stopped and wrinkled her forehead. She didn't seem inclined to say anything more, so I figured she was waiting for me to say something. "Yes, Thelma, I think a living will is a good idea. Is there some way I can help?"

"Well, I just wasn't sure about who has to sign it. It was a little confusing, but I was hoping if you signed it next to my name, it would be okay."

"I can witness it for you, Thelma. That's no problem."

"The form calls for the signature of a 'neutered republic.' Are you one of them?"

I was momentarily confused, and just as I was about to ask her to repeat her comment, I realized what she was saying. "Do you mean a notary public?" I asked and couldn't help chuckling.

"Oh, that's how you say it. Are you one of those?" she asked.

I smiled and informed her that even though I was not a notary public, I could sign as a witness and that would be sufficient.

Patients are precious. Maybe I'll ask my wife tonight if she thinks I'm a "neutered republic."

Hmmm, then again, maybe I won't.

Facts
AND
Perspectives

Facts shaping perspectives

makes good sense,

but perspectives shaping facts

is simply wrong.

The Unexpected
Double
Whammy

Oxygen is our lifeblood. If the passageway to our lungs is blocked, oxygen has no corridor to our heart and brain and we die—simple as that.

In His Image, by Dr. Paul Brand, provides a summary of the ongoing human struggle to maintain life: "We are, all of us, five minutes from death. Life depends on our ability to stay in contact with the vital element of oxygen around us. When deprived of air for any length of time, the patient turns blue."

My medical school professors taught a similar lesson using slightly different words, and long ago I had resolved to never forget it.

If the all-important oxygen transfer doesn't happen, we die.

Tick-tock, tick-tock . . . As the seconds of our lives slowly ebb away, death is never more than five minutes from becoming an actuality. Sure, there are the occasional miraculous stories of drowning victims or hypothermic patients coming back to life after extended absences, but generally five minutes without oxygen brings about our demise.

ها ها ها

HE WAS JITTERY, NERVOUS, and sweating profusely. He stuttered and shivered, finally gasping, "The bees got me . . . stung me . . . a bunch of 'em!"

I asked a few questions, gaining little information other than his denial of any prior problems with bee stings. He looked to be about thirty years old and was panting, with loud wheezing accompanying his every breath. His struggle to suck air into his lungs was obvious and clearly my number-one priority.

He's in real trouble and lucky he was so close to the hospital.

I rattled off a summary: "Okay, Travis, let me get this straight. About fifteen minutes ago at a softball game, you were stung three times, and right after that you started to feel cold and shaky. Over the last five minutes you've started to have trouble catching your breath. Is that about right?"

He nodded vigorously. The pieces of the puzzle—events and symptoms and physical signs—came together. Travis's day of fun in the sun changed dramatically a few minutes after being stung. His friends rushed him to the emergency room, and my initial evaluation revealed that he was suffering from a severe allergic reaction that was rapidly evolving into a life-threatening emergency.

The tubes leading to his lungs are squeezing shut and catastrophe may be right around the corner. His heart is pumping for all it's worth, but to no avail. I need to reverse this process—fast!

A frightening reminder drifted through my consciousness.

If the all-important oxygen transfer doesn't happen, we die.

When he started making a high-pitched whistling sound as he breathed out, I knew there wasn't much time to think. The heaving chest muscles looked impressive but accomplished little. His fear-stricken dilated eyes conveyed a simple, wordless message: *Please! . . . Please, Doc! . . . Help me! . . . I'm dying!*

Color changes underscored the intensity of his distress: blue lips, ashen face, and bright red starburst hemorrhages overlying the whites of his eyes.

The nurse reported his blood pressure at 200/100 with a heart rate of 130. His eyes jerked back and forth, left to right, right to left, searching desperately, anywhere, for relief. As he gasped and trembled, his alertness was waning.

The unnecessary cue again floated through my mind.

If the all-important oxygen transfer doesn't happen, we die.

I looked at the nurse and said, "Please start an IV with normal saline and place an oxygen mask at high flow. Also prepare for adrenaline injection—standard dose." (Adrenaline is an injectable emergency medication used in various crisis situations.)

She shifted into high gear, skillfully inserting an intravenous line into his arm and attaching a bag of saline. She applied an oxygen mask to his face and drew liquid adrenaline into a syringe.

For the simple reason that time was working against me, I decided to inject the potentially lifesaving adrenaline directly into his vein rather than going the customary route of injecting it into the fatty tissue underneath his skin. He was in severe distress and obviously starting to tire. Without hesitation I injected the medicine straight-line into the vein, knowing it would reach the heart and lungs within seconds.

The fluid surged down the transparent plastic tubing and rapidly entered his circulation. I stared intently at Travis, looking for any changes. He was slipping away from me and could no longer muster words. A sleep born of exhaustion was overtaking him, and I knew he might never wake.

Come on, Travis, stay with me! You can do it. You're young and strong, and relief is on the way.

I said a silent prayer.

Seconds passed . . . stretching into a half minute . . . I was just beginning to consider giving another dose of adrenaline when finally something started to happen. Yes, there it was: his chest expansion increased ever so slightly. Almost imperceptibly Travis started to draw more air into his lungs, and his whistling wheezing diminished. Once again the all-important oxygen transfer necessary for survival was taking place. His face flooded with relief as he gulped air as though it were water. The constricted breathing tubes were finally freed from the effects of the bee stings. I listened to his chest; his lungs were moving a lot of air in and out and doing so without any apparent difficulty.

I sighed, grateful that the crisis had been thwarted. His bluish lips reverted to a more normal rose color, and the ashen gray hue of death departed from his face.

He pulled off his oxygen mask and said, "Thank you! Thank you so much, Doc."

I smiled and said, "You're welcome, Travis. You're doing a whole lot better. Try to relax and breathe slowly. I don't want you to hyperventilate. I'm going to keep a close eye on you for a little while."

"Good work," I said to the nurse and walked over to a desk to write a note in his chart.

In the next moment the quiet afterglow of a job well done was shattered by a low, twisted groan that ended in a whispered shriek. "My chest, my chest! Help me! Get the weight off me!"

I whirled around to see Travis clutching at his chest. I realized in an instant that everything had turned upside down—and I knew why: the adrenaline had not only granted relief to the constricted bronchial tubes, but the sudden onslaught of the drug had driven his heart into a racing mass of muscle. Now each beat of his heart was accompanied by an exaggerated contraction with more than ten times the normal amount of power. My stomach turned. This drug-induced insult could lead to a deadly deterioration of his heart's rhythm.

What the devil? Why is Travis reacting with such hypersensitivity to the adrenaline? He can't tolerate this very long. His heart will fibrillate, and then I might lose him.

The room's atmosphere had turned ominous in a hurry. A logical explanation for what was happening eluded me. All I knew for sure was that my decision to inject the adrenaline intravenously was backfiring in a big way, and I broke into a cold sweat as I considered my options.

Think, Scott! Travis was stung by bees, and shortly thereafter he reacted with trouble breathing. When he arrived he was gasping and wheezing with a rapid heart rate and clammy skin. I calculated how much adrenaline to give and injected it intravenously because of the severity of his crisis. What's gone wrong?

I took a moment to recalculate the dose.

Yes, the dose is right. Should I have used less adrenaline? Did I really need to inject it intravenously?

I was frightened for Travis and nervous for myself. The queasiness in my stomach seemed like an accusation. I did a quick exam: heart rate 140, blood pressure 220/120, heart sounds thumping ferociously and far too loudly. He was in serious trouble.

I need to do something fast. Most young guys handle this dose of adrenaline with no problem, but obviously Travis isn't, so I'll have to do whatever it takes to slow his frenzied heart—and do it now!

Travis rasped, "Help me!" and tore at his shirt to get relief from the pressure on his chest.

Okay, no more time to think. I need to counteract this adrenaline reaction.

With a rat-a-tat delivery, my words echoed off the emergency room walls in a staccato rhythm: "Nurse, IV rate to full, resume oxygen, and draw up one milligram of Inderal, and let's get ready for intravenous injection." (Inderal can serve as an antidote to adrenaline.)

The familiar chorus once again played its disturbing tune in my head.

If the all-important oxygen transfer doesn't happen, we die. . . . This can't be happening!

With the nurse holding the syringe at the ready, time froze. I watched his chest move with an exaggerated rising and falling. I waited a few seconds more, hoping for Travis to pull through this crisis on his own. I did not want to inject the Inderal because it could put me right back where I started when Travis originally showed up in the ER—the wheezing in his lungs might return with a vengeance.

If his heart muscle doesn't settle down, his blood pressure will collapse and drop like a rock. Shock will follow, and all this because of my aggressive decision to use the intravenous route. Travis may die, and if he does, his death will be my doing.

The seconds ticking by on the wall clock were loud and unnerving. Since Travis had grabbed his chest and complained of pressure, less than two minutes had passed. The words "inject the Inderal" were on the tip of my tongue when I sensed rather than saw that something had changed. His face slackened, ever so slightly. I felt his pulse: it had dropped—just a little, but it had dropped. His chest was heaving just a tad less than before. I held my breath and said nothing. I listened to his lungs.

I am not alone in being haunted by a patient outcome; most physicians carry regrets and would have appreciated the opportunity to have an occasional mulligan.

He's definitely moving more air. His eyes are calmer, and the crazed look of fear is gone. His breathing is slowing. Yes, the adrenaline is starting to pass from his system; his body is breaking it down and getting rid of it. Hallelujah . . . man alive! . . . hallelujah.

Sure enough, in the next couple of minutes, Travis's blood pressure and heart rate began to normalize. Another minute brought a look of relief to his face, and he smiled drowsily. He had just undergone an incredible workout, and he was drained.

It had all come full circle: I had seen the relief of the initial emergency followed by a far different crisis, one of my own making. I breathed deeply with inner thanksgiving. The fear that my aggressive approach might kill him drifted away—mercifully. My mind was quieted, and I thanked God that Travis was going to be okay.

Follow-up lab tests confirmed all systems were normal. Breathing, pulse, and oxygen levels revealed that the crisis was over. Travis had weathered the storm, but I observed him in the ER for another hour anyway just to be certain that no boomerang effect would occur.

He did well. The bee sting venom had spent itself, and his body had metabolized the adrenaline. His lung function returned to normal. I removed his IV and oxygen mask and watched him enjoy some apple juice. I prescribed an EpiPen (self-administered adrenaline kit) for any future bee sting emergency and advised him to follow up with his family doctor regarding long-term management.

᭞ ᭞ ᭞

THE DOUBLE WHAMMY NATURE of Travis's ER visit—solve one problem and, presto, there's another—insured that our time together would not be forgotten. **"Expect the unexpected"** was a lesson I learned the hard way that day, and for a long time "the bee sting patient" troubled my mind with the exhortation to be ready for anything because surprises are the norm in the world of emergency room care. Thankfully I can remember this gut-wrenching encounter, not from the perspective that my aggressive decision-making led to a tragedy, but instead celebrating the simple fact that Travis ultimately gained relief.

A final comment deserves mention. I am not alone in being haunted by a patient outcome; most physicians carry regrets and would have appreciated the opportunity to have an occasional mulligan. But medicine doesn't grant do-overs, and so we live with our unfavorable consequences.

I have learned that

lingering self-incrimination

serves a valuable purpose

by etching forever in my mind

those occasions of flawed judgment.

The luxury of forgetting

is not a reprieve I seek.

Patients Share
the Blame

S arah was a pleasant, thirty-five-year-old woman arriving in the emergency room after a few weeks of deteriorating health. Her energy level had plummeted, and her skin was jaundiced. Her feet were so swollen she could wear only sandals. What did her laboratory tests show? Her liver enzymes were over eighteen thousand, while normal values should be less than fifty. What was her diagnosis? After reviewing her history, doing a physical exam, and performing further tests, I concluded she was suffering from liver failure due to a statin drug prescribed six weeks earlier to lower her cholesterol.

"Sarah, the cholesterol-lowering drug you're taking is a member of a family of drugs called statins and is the likely cause of your problems—fatigue, swelling, and, most importantly, liver failure. Do you remember what your cholesterol was when you started taking the medicine a few weeks ago?"

"I don't remember, Doctor, and I'm a little embarrassed with myself for not knowing. My doctor called a couple of days after my physical and told me my cholesterol was a little high. He thought it would be a good idea for me to take a medicine to lower it. He told me the drug was safe and could help reduce my long-term risk for heart disease, so I went along with his suggestion. Now I'm second-guessing my decision."

I shrugged. "I can understand that, but doctors never know in advance how a drug will affect a patient, and there's no question statins can reduce the risk of a heart attack. Personally I think they've been overused and their side effects minimized. You'll have to review the situation with your family doctor later, but I'm taking you off the statin immediately, and we need to keep you here in the hospital for a few days and watch your liver enzymes."

⁊ ⁊ ⁊

WHEN I STOPPED BY HER ROOM to see her four days later, I was very pleased to be able to say, "Sarah, I see that your lab tests are much better since the statin has been removed, and your liver is healing now."

Sarah smiled and replied, "I'm feeling so much better, and thank you for your help."

"No problem."

"Dr. Jensen, I never felt as miserable as I did the night I came to the hospital, and I know I'm lucky to have recovered so rapidly. I don't intend to take that drug again, but what if my doctor recommends giving it another try? What would you do if you were me?"

"Sarah, I'm a skeptic. A study done several years ago showed that only one out of fifty patients taking a statin drug received the benefit the researchers were hoping for. But the pharmaceutical company analyzed the same data and claimed that its statin drug lowered the risk of a heart attack by forty percent. Statistics can be manipulated in lots of different ways. I'm a guy who thinks that if forty-nine out of fifty people are going to receive no measurable benefit, I'm not likely to take the pill. But to answer your question, Sarah, I don't think you should ever take a statin drug again."

"Are you saying that the same study results can be interpreted in two entirely different ways? One view claims a forty percent reduction in heart attack risk while a different perspective declares that only one out of fifty patients will get the hoped-for benefit. That's crazy."

"It's the truth. When you get the chance, Google 'NNT.' It's short for 'Number Needed to Treat' and refers to the number of patients needing to be treated in order for one patient to receive the expected result. Sarah, our society is overrun with pharmaceutical companies advertising and selling their drugs and vaccines, and these marketing folks know their business.

Most people don't have a clue how many pills Americans take. It's a fact that even though the United States accounts for only five percent of the world's population, we consume over half of all the world's prescription drugs."

≈ ≈ ≈

SARAH'S STORY IS NOT UNUSUAL, because many people assume that if a medicine is recommended by a doctor and approved by the Food and Drug Administration, it must be okay. Her casual acceptance and naiveté could have cost far more than a few days in the hospital.

A powerful lesson emerges from Sarah's medical adventure: virtually any intervention can cause significant harm as well as provide benefit. As much as possible, patients need to do some research when it comes to interventions—pills, surgery, or whatever—because things aren't the way they used to be. The big-business agenda for health care focuses on the almighty dollar, leaving all of us with the warning: **interventions that appear safe and well-intended can still be lethal and unnecessary.**

Primary care physicians must strive to keep their patients out of harm's way because over-zealous doctors may act without fully considering the risk of the intervention, whether it be surgery, chemotherapy, radiation, medication, or a procedure. I am oft reminded of the adage, **if the only tool carried by a carpenter is a hammer, everything he sees looks like a nail.**

≈ ≈ ≈

"I DON'T KNOW, Neal, that may not be such a good idea."

"What do you mean, Doc?"

"I think you're doing pretty well. Your symptoms are minimal and not like your previous heart complaints. Ordering an angiogram is a serious step," I warned, referring to a test involving the injection of dye into blood vessels supplying the heart muscle, "and you've already had several done with multiple stents being placed at different times."

"I know, Doc, but I would really appreciate some reassurance that this weird chest tightness is not coming from my heart."

"Neal, you had your first heart attack when you were forty years old, and since then you've managed to do okay for twenty-five years. But you're older now, and you have developed diabetes. Just because you haven't experienced complications from this test previously doesn't mean everything will go smoothly next time around. Your symptoms aren't exertional, and they don't match up with typical heart complaints. You said yourself the tight feeling lasts only a few seconds, and that isn't characteristic of heart pain. Furthermore your EKG is okay; it shows no evidence that your heart is causing any problems."

"But I do feel a little short of breath sometimes when the pain hits," Neal protested.

How do I convince Neal that an angiogram contains real risk? Stroke, heart attack, or blood clots are all potential dangers, especially with his history of diabetes. On the other hand, if I'm wrong and he's right, I'll have to live with that for the rest of my life.

"Let's do this, Neal. I'll contact a cardiologist and review your situation with him. We'll have the specialist weigh in on this decision."

"Sounds good, Doc. Thanks for being flexible. I appreciate it."

I arranged for a cardiologist to see Neal the next day, and sure enough, an angiogram was ordered. I figured Neal had pushed the heart doctor pretty hard.

Unfortunately, things didn't go as smoothly as Neal hoped. The vessels in his heart were fine and required no stents or specific intervention, but a large blood clot formed in his groin where the angiographic catheter was inserted (so it could be threaded through the aorta to the heart). A piece of the blood clot floated downstream and blocked the flow of blood to his lower leg. He had to have an operation in which a surgeon removed the clot. The blood flow was restored, but he suffered kidney damage during the surgery and had to stay in the hospital for two weeks. When he was discharged, he could not manage at home, so off to the nursing home he went.

An overnight procedure turned into a two-week hospitalization that led to a three-week stay in a nursing home for therapy and convalescence. Neal recovered some but never returned to his previous level of health and activity. His desire for reassurance regarding some nonspecific symptoms altered his life forever and almost killed him.

๑ ๑ ๑

IT IS CRITICAL that patients recognize their own role in the use of dangerous interventions. Physicians do not operate in a vacuum in managing their patients' health. Patients may passively accept, as in Sarah's misadventure, but they may also encourage difficulties by pursuing a guarantee that "all is well," as in Neal's calamity.

The desire to hear the words, "You are in good health, and there is no evidence of heart disease or cancer," can be as powerful an addiction as the strongest narcotic. Utilizing needless interventions for the sole purpose of reassurance can unwittingly invite catastrophe into a patient's life. Consider that one or two people out of every hundred undergoing an angiogram will suffer a significant complication such as heart attack, stroke, or blood clot. Recognize that contrast material used in CAT scans damages the kidneys of thousands of patients every year. Patients must bear in mind this question: "How much am I willing to risk for the elusive and short-lived gift of reassurance?"

The "want" of a patient is not equivalent to a "need" of the patient, and when the "want" serves as the sole driver for ordering tests and other interventions, avoidable and disastrous outcomes will occur—it's just a matter of time. Patients must own the fact that they play a very real role in the overindulgent extravaganza of health care utilization and need to recognize that too much of a good thing is probably just that—too much. And the danger that lurks within virtually any intervention is not easily recognized until it manifests itself, and by then, it is too late. When a patient faces decision time in the world of health care, the following questions may help differentiate the "need" from the "want":

1. Is this medicine or test or surgery really necessary?
2. What are the risks and the benefits, short term and long term?
3. Are the risks more likely to occur than the benefits?
4. How many people need to be treated for one person
    to receive the intended benefit?
5. If roles were reversed, what would the doctor do?

These queries can help a patient consider options more carefully and possibly provide the stimulus to say, "Doc, I'm not sure this is the direction I want to go. While reassurance sounds nice, I think I better consider the downside of things. I'll chew on it before moving forward."

(Googling the "NNT" statistic is a quick way to get an idea of the likely benefit from a proposed intervention—medication, vaccine, surgery, etc. For example, a flu shot is marketed as a means of reducing the complication of flu-associated pneumonia, but an NNT analysis reveals that out of a hundred patients receiving a flu shot, only one would actually receive the benefit of avoiding pneumonia.

◈ ◈ ◈

HAROLD WAS AN ELDERLY PATIENT with significant medical issues and an abundance of common sense. The following conversation we had a few months before his death explores the difference between a "want" and a "need," and informs the notion that patients must remain ever vigilant in the glitzy and extravagant system of health care we enjoy today.

> **HAROLD:** Doc, this cancer medicine is expensive and makes me dopey. Now I've got a rash all over my body, and I itch constantly. If this pill does what the cancer specialist hopes for, how will it affect my cancer?
>
> **ME:** Well, it's impossible to say, but it could give you some extra time—anywhere from a few weeks to a few months.
>
> **HAROLD:** Then I'm going to stop it. I'd rather be comfortable while I'm here and die sooner. I'm going to be checking out sooner rather than later, and I don't want to live my final days itching and miserable. Thanks, Doc, for your help and your candor.

Harold stopped the medicine and shortly thereafter felt a whole lot better. For a few weeks he was able to live without the curse of constant itching and scratching. When he died peacefully a couple months later, his family expressed appreciation that the noxious chemo drug had been stopped. **When it's decision-making time, the difference between a "want" and a "need" must be carefully considered.**

Harold came to understand a simple truth about cancer treatments: if the price of adding a couple months to his life meant the remainder of his time on earth would be sheer misery, he would rather skip the extra time and enjoy whatever good-quality days he had left.

The fact that medical science can accomplish a certain feat (e.g. extending life by a few months) can create a dilemma, because a procedure granting significant benefit for one patient can cause nothing but wretchedness for another. **What medical science can do often runs counter to what should be done.** The trust a patient invests in his doctor should be reciprocated by the advocacy the doctor carries out on the patient's behalf, and this calls for recognition that "no intervention" could be a better choice than a knee-jerk reflex to "do something." A patient may assume his doctor is considering the risks as well as the potential benefits when a procedure is ordered or a medication prescribed, but such an assumption may represent a grave error of judgment. **If at all possible, the patient must insist on being a fully participative partner in decision-making in order for optimal medical care to occur—the voice of the patient is critical.**

OFFERING A
DIFFERENT PERSPECTIVE

Our visit had been trying. Lila had more or less asked the same question about her problem with leaking urine at least four times: How are you going to fix me? When will you give me a pill that works? Why haven't you been able to solve this? What are you going to try today?

I knew what I had to say, but her unbending insistence that I solve her issue made me pause to reconsider.

Am I missing something? Should I be more aggressive in managing this issue?

"Lila, I have tried virtually every pill I can to help you with your urinary leakage, and none of them have done the trick. You've had reactions to most of the medicines, and the ones you could tolerate didn't do you any good. The pills you took created a lot of new concerns, including dry mouth, constipation, cramping, fatigue, and weakness. And I really don't think you're a good candidate for any of the surgical procedures that are sometimes used for this problem."

I paused, but Lila said nothing. "I honestly think, Lila, that the best course of action here is to not try any further medications and certainly to avoid surgery. You've been successful in making some lifestyle adjustments with this leakage. I'm sorry, but I think you'll simply have to live with the fact that your bladder dribbles occasionally, and you'll just have to deal with it the best you can."

Finally she responded, but I wasn't prepared for the onslaught of her words. With a voice rising in pitch and surprisingly loud, she exclaimed, "You mean I have to live with this for the rest of my life?"

She is not making this easy, and she is not going to be happy—but here goes.

I composed my thoughts and pushed her chart back toward a far corner of the desk. I leaned toward her and gazed directly at her eyes. "Lila, you're ninety-nine years old. In five months you'll turn a hundred. Who knows how long you'll have to live with this?"

As I waited for a response, I noticed she had clenched her jaw and pursed her lips. I wondered if I had been too blunt.

Darn it! I should have said that differently. I didn't mean to offend her.

But finally, Lila's face broke into a grin, and she chuckled, saying, "Oh, I see what you mean. Of course, it's true—I guess I am pretty old. Yeah, I suppose things could be worse."

I smiled and nodded my agreement, realizing that the most important thing I was able to do for Lila that day was a little attitude adjustment. Her medical problems needed to be viewed from a different vantage point: age, prognosis, and lifestyle had to be considered alongside the risks associated with available interventions. **Offering a different perspective can solve a lot of problems, and more frequently than I like, it's the only contribution I can make.**

≈ ≈ ≈

"Doc, you rock!"

It was nice to hear Tim's chuckling voice on the other end of the line after I told him that the medicine he was taking for gout had cut the amount of uric acid in his blood in half. Uric acid is a natural by-product of everyday activities in the human body, but its accumulation causes gout. Tim's level was now tiny, and a recurrence of gout was highly unlikely. He was ecstatic, and I was pleased and satisfied that our mutual efforts had brought him relief.

Tim and I had spent considerable time together working to control his condition. His attacks had been unpredictable, hitting with a vengeance and laying him up for weeks at a time.

Tim added, "You know, Doc, it's been a long time since I've had an attack; I'm sure it's been more than a year. Thanks so much."

Our achievement was in large part due to the teaching and learning that went on between doctor and patient.

Tim's story reminded me of an old adage: "Give a man a fish and he will eat for a day; teach a man to fish and he will eat for a lifetime." Before success could be achieved, I had needed to confront Tim with the reality that the only way we could stabilize his disabling gout was to work together. I pushed hard to sell him on the idea that a daily pill would be necessary to prevent recurrences of gout. We had failed with other approaches, and this option was all I had left to offer. I recalled the conversation vividly.

"Tim, I can't solve this problem alone. You have to do the work. I can help, and the pills can do their part, but it's you who has to make the effort to understand the disease and take the medicine to eliminate the attacks. I know you're a tough guy, but I'm telling you right now that in a battle between you and gout, the gout will win every time."

Those were the words I used to teach him of the value of preventive medicine. My comments provided a different perspective: one with Tim as the leader and me as the navigator. That day my words did their job and a lesson emerged: **teaching is fortified by selling, and patient buy-in is essential for success.**

While science may be the foundation of our discipline, the art of medicine calls for sales skills with a constant focus on the patient's viewpoint.

These encounters with Lila and Tim are especially pertinent as doctors are forced to engage patients in a productivity-driven model. Assembly-line medical visits, intervening computer screens, and a lack of time to build relationships combine to convey an unfortunate message to the patient: "Sorry, but there's no time for further questions. Maybe the Internet can give you what you need. On your way out, the receptionist will provide you with a handout regarding today's visit." If this is the kind of service a patient is getting, the doctor's recommendations are not likely to count for much, and the desired results are not likely to happen—it's as simple as that.

A physician's perspective doesn't become the patient's perspective merely because of words. Taking the time and making the effort to be persuasive without using any bullying techniques can go a long way toward convincing a patient to get on board with the doctor's recommendation.

When Two Sounds
Are Better
than One

*L*ub . . . *Dub* . . . *Lub* . . . *Dub* . . . *Lub* . . . *Dub* . . . goes the heart with its cyclic thumping noises, never ceasing to remind me of the critical and delicate function of its valves. But sometimes something can go wrong.

"Dr. Jensen, Henry Wilson, a sixty-five-year-old patient of yours, is here in the emergency room and doesn't look good: he's in big trouble and going downhill fast. I'm not sure what brought this on, but his heart is failing—his lungs are filling up with fluid." With those few words, a crisis had been presented and a response demanded. The edge to Dr. Will Levine's voice over the phone conveyed far more urgency than his words.

I was instantly engaged, and my mind hummed with possibilities as to what might cause Henry to go into what sounded like heart failure. Dr. Levine was a seasoned physician not prone to exaggeration.

I wonder what's happening with Henry. Two weeks ago in the office he was in great spirits and had no complaints whatsoever.

Dr. Levine further summarized Henry's complaints, saying, "Two hours ago, Henry experienced the sudden onset of difficulty breathing. He was instantly short of breath. In the last ten minutes, he started gasping for air; fortunately, he got a little relief from the supplemental oxygen I gave him. He denies any typical symptoms of heart attack—no chest pain, no nausea, and no jaw or arm pain."

"What's his exam show?" I asked.

"Fluid in both lungs," Dr. Levine responded, "and his heart's going way too fast at 120. I heard a mechanical click in the aortic region, so I figured he had his aortic valve replaced."

Translated into nonmedical lingo, Dr. Levine had just advised me that Henry's heart muscle couldn't keep up with the demands being made on it. Fluid was backing up into the lungs like a highway traffic jam, and this accumulation prevented the necessary oxygen exchange from taking place, because the lungs were no longer light and airy, but more like a wet sponge. It would only be a matter of time before the low oxygen content in his blood threatened Henry's vital organs. Dr. Levine had also identified a mechanical *click* coming from Henry's artificial heart valve, and indeed, Henry had had his aortic valve replaced several years earlier. Normally each contraction of the heart produces two soft valve-based sounds heard with a stethoscope: *Lub . . . dub . . . lub . . . dub.* Henry's aortic valve had been surgically replaced, so a loud "click" replaced the customary soft "dub" sound giving a *Lub . . . click . . . lub . . . click* pattern.

But hold on . . .

My brain was protesting. Something wasn't quite right!

"Dr. Levine, what other valve sounds did you hear?"

"None." He paused. "The aortic click was loud enough to mask anything else. Why?"

"You should actually hear two separate *click* sounds, because Henry had both his aortic and mitral valves replaced. I've listened to his heart many times, and it makes a *click-click* sound, which is pretty unique. There should definitely be a double click, and it's actually quite prominent."

Dr. Levine said, "Let me recheck his heart. I'll be back in a minute."

I waited uneasily until finally he was back on the line.

"Dr. Jensen, I'm not hearing two mechanical valve sounds. There is only one *click,* and it's loudest over the aortic region, so it's probably coming from his aortic valve. There is no mitral valve sound at all. That's odd."

"Let's get a bedside echocardiogram, stat! Please get back to me ASAP. Also contact cardiology and tell them we've got a crisis brewing. Henry may need emergency surgery. Thanks so much."

The heart ultrasound would help us decide the next steps and could be accomplished quickly. When Dr. Levine called back a few minutes later, the excitement in his voice was impossible to miss.

"Dr. Jensen, it's pretty amazing! The echocardiogram shows the artificial mitral valve is stuck wide open due to a huge blood clot. It looks like the clot formed within the jaws of the mitral valve leaflets, preventing the valve from closing, so the blood sloshes back and forth with each contraction. His heart is doing double duty with each contraction, and it can't keep up. I've called for an emergency transfer to the heart hospital."

"Great job, Dr. Levine! I really appreciate it; keep me posted." And I signed off.

Things moved awfully fast for Henry in the next few minutes. Intravenous medications were injected to reduce stress on the heart, pulling fluid from his lungs. Supplemental oxygen was pushed to the max. He was transferred by ambulance to a hospital specializing in cardiac surgery and was in the operating room in less than an hour. The surgeon removed the blood clot and repaired the valve leaflets. Henry did well and was discharged after only five days in the hospital. His brush with death was soon a distant memory.

≈ ≈ ≈

Never lose sight of the value of direct communication, even if it takes more time and effort.

THIS STORY IMPARTS several key concepts. Medicine has advanced to a point whereby a patient can have open heart surgery on a Monday and be back home recuperating by Friday, with a return to work a week later. We are blessed to live during a time in which many causes of past human suffering have been alleviated or even eradicated, and a spirit of thankfulness for our pioneering ancestors would not be inappropriate. Their labors bring credence to the notion that the science fiction ideas of yesterday give rise to the tools of healing for today.

This story especially highlights an important truth in today's world of electronic medical records: patient care can be immensely improved by the simple act of a physician picking up the phone and speaking directly with a colleague about the patient's status. When physicians choose to accept as "good enough" the communication occurring through typical avenues—transcription, faxes, mail, or electronic health records (EHR)—precious time and vital firsthand understanding may be sacrificed, and the patient may suffer—needlessly. It's ironic and more than a little dangerous that widespread public perception assumes that EHRs are faster and better than the old-fashioned method of simply talking with another person. This simply isn't true. Few EHRs possess the ability to communicate with one another, and it is not uncommon for vital medical information to simply be "dumped" into a computer file never to be appreciated or utilized.

Direct discussions between doctors regarding the specifics of a patient's care are discouraged by the very nature of the factory-line dictates of our EHR-driven health care system. Henry would have died were it not for rapid diagnosis and surgery, and Dr. Levine almost certainly saved his life by contacting me directly. Had he been satisfied with leaving a message, sending a fax, or simply entering his findings into an electronic health record, our efforts would likely have been too little, too late.

THE PHYSICIAN'S ROLE AS PATIENT ADVOCATE

DEMANDS THAT THE VALUE OF

DIRECT DOCTOR-TO-DOCTOR COMMUNICATION

BE RECOGNIZED AND HONORED,

FOR ANY OTHER ATTITUDE INVITES DISASTER

FOR THOSE WHO SEEK OUR HELP.

Be Careful What
You
Ask For

"Doc, what about a CAT scan of my lungs?"

"What do you mean, Bill? What's this about a CAT scan? Is there a problem with your lungs?"

"Well, no, but a friend of mine died from lung cancer, which might have been connected with some asbestos exposure many years ago. So I got to thinking, *What if I had some exposure I didn't know about?*"

I thought a moment. "I see. Bill, did your friend smoke cigarettes?"

"Yeah, he smoked like a chimney—couple packs a day, every day—right up to his last breath."

Bill had no risk factors for lung cancer and no symptoms. I advised him that a CAT scan wasn't needed. I shared with him that the contrast material used during a CAT scan of his chest could cause kidney damage and other problems. I also told him something else.

"Bill, I'm sorry about your friend's death, but in all honesty, I suspect his cancer had nothing to do with asbestos and everything to do with tobacco. You don't smoke and never have. You don't have any known exposures that would put you at risk for lung cancer. In your situation, I think the risk of the scan would exceed any potential benefit."

"Oh, I see. I was just thinking a little reassurance would be nice, but what you're saying makes sense."

"I tell you what, Bill. Think it over and read this essay about health care entitled, "Mrs. Bear's Final Illness—a Mole That Became a Mountain." Call me in a few days and tell me how you want to proceed."

I handed him a five-page story, hoping he would read it.

A week later, Bill called and said, "I've decided to skip the CAT scan. I don't have any complaints, and I feel good. I think my buddy's death spooked me a little, but I feel a lot better after discussing it with you. That paper you gave me about Mrs. Bear was pretty good. Thanks for taking the time to talk."

I hung up and smiled.

I'm glad I spoke with Bill so candidly and took the time to chat—that might have been the most important conversation I had all day.

๑ ๑ ๑

"Do you think I should get a steroid injection, Doc?"

"I'm not sure I understand what you're asking, Bob. You told me a few minutes ago you've been feeling pretty good. What's this about an injection?"

"You know, Doc. My back—it's been a problem forever—and a buddy of mine got an injection and told me it was like a miracle!"

I asked Bob about his pain and learned that he had spent a good share of the summer going up and down a ladder painting his house. His chronic back pain had behaved pretty well, but he did have some occasional mild symptoms. Even though his back hadn't been this good in years, he was impressed with his friend's glowing report about a near-miraculous injection.

"Bob, I know you've had problems with your back for a long time, and I appreciate the fact you have arthritis and disc disease, but really, with a little ibuprofen and an occasional muscle relaxant, you've done well."

"Yeah, I know, Doc, but it still bothers me some, and I don't like taking pills."

"Bob, I want to tell you about a patient who died a couple years ago. Let's call him John Doe. Anyway, quite a while back he decided to undergo an elective procedure in his low back area. A needle was inserted into his back and was never supposed to come anywhere near any nerves. Nevertheless the needle tip did strike a nerve. In an instant his life changed forever, and for more than a decade John Doe suffered recurring, piercing pain. He tried pills and he tried therapy, with no relief. Finally, after some of the pain medications damaged his kidneys, he gave up and lived with the pain. Every day he felt intermittent, stabbing discomfort. All this came from an elective injection—one which he chose—and he had to live with that reality till the day he died."

Bob decided to mull things over and talk with his wife. I also gave him a copy of the parable, "Mrs. Bear's Final Illness—a Mole That Became a Mountain." He called me the following week and said, "My back's doing okay, and I can get along with the symptoms pretty easily. I'm going to skip that injection. And by the way, Dr. Jensen, my wife and I both enjoyed the story about the animals."

◢◣ ◢◣ ◢◣

THESE TWO PATIENTS were seen in the space of a couple hours on a Thursday morning, and both ended up declining the very intervention they had requested. A review of risks and benefits along with the message from the parable about "Mrs. Bear" helped Bill and Bob consider a different perspective. The overarching factor of importance was the existence of a relationship built on trust and advocacy—Bill and Bob both trusted my opinion while I advocated for them by sharing information born of experience and scientific expertise. I didn't insist that my viewpoint rule the day, and I welcomed the chance to address their concerns.

The role of patient advocate calls on me to use different skill sets: sometimes I'm a salesman, sometimes I'm a scientist, sometimes I'm a counselor, and often I'm a skeptic. But almost always, if I advocate for a patient by treating him as if he were a member of my family, I will serve him well.

I have distributed the animal fable "Mrs. Bear's Final Illness—a Mole That Became a Mountain" to patients for twenty years, and the author, Richard Feinstein, has been so kind as to grant me permission to include it in this chapter. It is one of many essays published in his book *Ethical Conflicts in Daily Medical Practice.* With thanks to Dr. Feinstein, please enjoy this powerful fable that reinforces the teaching, **be careful what you ask for; you might get more than you bargained for.**

Mrs. Bear's Final Illness—*a Mole That Became a Mountain*
By Richard Feinstein, MD, Dermatologist

We are living in a society of medical specialists: technocrats who sometimes treat patients as examples of diseases rather than as humans suffering with illness. Each goes about taking care of what he knows best, sometimes forgetting that the diseased organ is just part of a sick patient. This phenomenon can be particularly tragic when the patient is elderly and where at times the judicious avoidance of certain examinations and treatments can be in the best interest of the patient. This animal fable has been written to call attention to this situation.

MRS. ALMA BEAR from Big Pine Junction was ninety-six years old. All members of the Bear Family from Big Pine had lived to be very old, and Mrs. Bear was older than most. Only recently had she developed signs of aging; her eyesight was failing, her hearing was failing, and she required the use of a cane when walking more than a few feet. She was, however, content with her life and not afraid to meet her maker, when her time was due.

One day after a bath, she noted a dark bump on the skin near her groin. She could see it plainly beneath the thinned white fur.

"I don't believe that I've ever seen that bump there before," she commented to herself.

After drying and dressing she called her daughter, who lived just down the road. Her daughter thought it best that the doctor have a look.

"I don't believe that it's anything serious at all," commented old Doctor Elk. "Your eyesight isn't as good as it used to be, Alma, and that little bump has probably been there for a good long time," he continued to Mrs. Bear and her daughter. "However, I think that it would be a good idea to take a biopsy of that bump, just to make sure."

So Mrs. Alma Bear was admitted to Big Pine Junction Memorial Hospital on a Tuesday afternoon. She signed the appropriate insurance forms, and waiver forms, and release forms, and was wheeled in a chair to her lovely room overlooking the dark green forest. She had a peaceful night and was awakened the next morning by a young coyote in a short white lab coat who came to take blood from her veins. After he left, the nurse, Miss Pigeon, arrived with a plastic bottle to collect a urine specimen. She also took Mrs. Bear's vital signs and recorded them on the medical chart. A young rabbit in a pink-and-white striped dress came into the room to deliver her breakfast tray. Mrs. Bear loved the scrambled eggs and bacon and toast, and sweet rolls and coffee, and was just finishing the last morsel when Doctor Elk stopped into the room.

"We're going to do some tests for a day or two, and then we'll have the surgeon perform the biopsy on the bump. Nothing to worry about at all." And then he was gone from the room.

Except for the delivery and removal of her food trays, she was completely alone the rest of the day. Her daughter visited her that evening, and after her daughter left, Mrs. Bear went to sleep. The next morning she was awakened while it was still dark by a female hippo nurse who gave her an enema. Another nurse helped get Mrs. Bear onto a stretcher, and she was taken to the radiology department. She had a kidney x-ray, a painful barium enema x-ray, and finally an upper gastrointestinal x-ray. She had had a series of chest x-rays on admission the day before. When she was returned to her room, her lunch tray was waiting for her, but she wasn't very hungry from all the tests, and didn't eat or drink anything. The door to her room opened, and an ox walked into the room wearing green pajamas and a long white coat.

"I'm Doctor Ox. There is a little shadow in your bladder that was visible on the x-rays that were performed this morning. I'm going to look into your bladder tomorrow morning with a special lighted instrument. I don't believe that there is anything seriously wrong, but it is a good idea to check and make sure." And then he was gone from the room.

Fifteen minutes later the door opened again and a young eagle walked into the room. He was also wearing green pajamas and a long white coat.

"I'm Doctor Eagle. There is a shadow that was discovered on the chest x-ray of your lungs. Tomorrow morning, after you finish with Doctor Ox, I will look down into your lung with a special lighted instrument called a bronchoscope. I don't believe that you have anything seriously wrong with your lung, but it is best to make certain." And then he was gone from the room.

A little later in the afternoon a groundhog entered the room. He too wore green pajamas and a white laboratory coat.

"I'm Doctor Groundhog. You have a small shadow that was discovered on the x-ray of your lower intestine. Tomorrow in the late afternoon, I will look into your lower bowel with a special lighted instrument called a sigmoidoscope. I don't believe that you have any serious problem in your lower bowel, but it is best to be certain." And then he too was gone from the room.

It was very late afternoon and the sun was setting. Mrs. Bear was regaining some interest in eating; she hadn't eaten or really even had anything to drink in over 24 hours. The door to her room opened quickly.

"Time for another enema," declared Miss Hippo as she burst into the room. She turned Mrs. Bear on her side. "We have to clean you out for those special tests tomorrow." When this was finished, Miss Hippo helped Mrs. Bear into a wheelchair for a short trip to the treatment room. Mrs. Bear was helped onto the examination table with her legs up on the cold stirrups, wide apart. She had not been in that position for many years, and it certainly felt uncomfortable. The door to the small treatment room opened and a porcupine, dressed in green pajamas and long white coat, entered the room. Without saying a word, he sat down on the stool that had been placed on the floor between Mrs. Bear's open legs by the nurse. He felt around the private parts of her body, and then placed a cold metal instrument inside her. He did some other things for a few minutes, and then he stood up and left the room.

It was dark outside when she returned to her room. She had lost her interest in eating, but removed the cover from her dinner tray to see what food had been delivered for her.

"Why have I been given this to eat?" she wondered out loud, looking at the small piece of dry fish and the cup of weak tea on her dinner tray.

"The doctor found an elevated blood sugar and has placed you on a special diet," answered the nurse, Miss Pigeon.

The next day came and Mrs. Bear was taken to a special room for her cystoscopy. She later had her bronchoscopy, and finally later in the day had a sigmoidoscopy test performed. She was returned to her room late in the day after the sun had set, too exhausted to have anything to eat or drink, and she went quickly to sleep.

She was awakened early the next morning by the nurse who inserted a rubber catheter into her bladder. A needle was placed into a vein on the top of her hand and fluid was administered into the vein by the nurse. Several medications were then injected into the rubber part of the tubing, and she felt herself getting sleepy and dizzy. She was placed on a stretcher and taken to the operating room for the biopsy of her skin bump. She did not remember anything else until later in the day when she awoke in the recovery room, where other patients were also on stretchers nearby.

"I'm having a lot of pain in my side," she mumbled to herself, not expecting anyone to answer.

"That is where you had the operation, Mrs. Bear," the nurse responded. "Doctor Beaver removed your skin bump; everything is going to be okay. It was only a little mole." The nurse then gave Mrs. Bear another injection into the rubber tubing, and Mrs. Bear went back into a deep sleep.

She did not awake again until late at night, back in her own room. The fluid from the hanging bottle was leaking from the needle into her skin and not into her vein as it was supposed to do. The pain in her side, where the operation was done, was so great that it hurt to breathe and so she took only very shallow breaths. The rubber catheter in her bladder introduced bacteria that attacked the lining of her bladder and eventually the infection ascended to her kidneys. Her body had been weakened by the lack of food for 72 hours, and the severe lack of fluids had caused her kidneys to fail. The shallow respirations caused collapse of portions of her lungs and finally pneumonia developed.

"Her condition is quite serious," Doctor Elk told Mrs. Bear's daughter. "She has a kidney infection, and pneumonia, and now her kidneys are failing. After all, she is ninety-five years old. She's badly dehydrated and very weak." Doctor Elk turned to leave the room. "We're doing our best, but it doesn't look good."

Mrs. Bear's daughter felt the burning tears roll down her cheeks. She saw her mother lying in a coma in a cubicle in the intensive care unit. Mrs. Bear was on a breathing machine, intravenous fluid feedings, cardiac monitoring, and had an indwelling rubber catheter in her bladder. The other cubicles were filled with other critically ill patients, many of whom were also moribund. There was a carnival-like atmosphere to the large fluorescent-lighted room. Doctors, nurses and other white-coated workers scurried about, performing their jobs. "This is so different from the dark green forest that mother loves so much," she muttered to herself as she left. She was going to return home to wait for the inevitable phone call that would notify her of her mother's death. "If only mother had discovered that bump on her skin much earlier," she cried to herself, "perhaps she could have been saved?"

๑ ๑ ๑

TWENTY-FIRST-CENTURY MEDICINE is not all cures and transplants; interventions are imbued with risk, and it is the shrewd patient who takes seriously the responsibility of saying yes or no to recommendations for tests or procedures. A strong connection with a physician can serve as an invaluable resource, and I fear the day may come when trust-based relationships will no longer be available to serve patients.

Technology, surgery, medications, and many other routine medical interventions can be beneficial or harmful. We don't always know how things will play out. **Candid—often awkward—discussions may be the only way to avoid unnecessary interventions.**

Mrs. Bear's daughter issues a final plea—"If only mother had discovered that bump on her skin much earlier"—and opens the door to unnerving questions: How could such a disaster occur? Was there a single guilty party in this sad saga of Mrs. Bear's final hour? Was it an overzealous doctor who should be convicted? Or was Mrs. Bear simply too submissive and, so the one to blame? Or was the real problem a medical system gone awry, doling out unnecessary and risky interventions driven by arbitrary protocols based on fears of litigation?

Mrs. Bear would probably have been better served by a trusted family doctor telling her, "This bump is not likely a problem. Let's just keep an eye on it for three months and then recheck it. That might be the best way to avoid a wild-goose chase that could result in calamity."

Unfortunately for Mrs. Bear, her "skin bump" opened the door to never-ending "downstream" tests and procedures that only her death could stop.

MEDICINE IS NOT ALL CURES AND TRANSPLANTS;
DISCUSSIONS MAY BE THE ONLY WAY
TO AVOID UNNECESSARY INTERVENTIONS.

Avoid
Dead Carpenters
in the
Living Room

"**B**ob, I just called to check on your progress. You said this morning you might wrap things up today. How are things going?"

"Oh, fine, Doc, just fine. I was just taking a little rest, but I think I'll be able to get everything done before I leave."

That's sort of odd.

It was my carpenter's third day on the job, and he'd done great work, but it was almost five o'clock.

If he wants to finish everything today, why would he take a rest?

"I'm sorry, Bob, maybe I misunderstood. Did you say you were taking a rest?"

"Yeah, I was just lying down for a bit."

What's going on? Why would he do that? That doesn't make sense.

"I don't understand. Why would you lie down if you're trying to finish things up?"

Bob chuckled and said, "Don't worry, Doc, I didn't use your couch. I just rested on the floor for a few minutes. I wasn't feeling so good."

Sliding into doctor mode, I said, "Bob, I don't care if you lie on the couch, but it seems odd to take a rest at five in the afternoon if you're trying to finish up. Tell me how you're not feeling well."

"Oh, it's nothing to worry about. I'm feeling better now, but my stomach was a little upset. I felt sort of nauseated. My bologna sandwich didn't sit right with me."

"Have you been having problems with your stomach?"

"Not really. I think it must have been some bad bologna," Bob replied.

"Hmmm. You said your stomach was upset and you were a little nauseated. Did you have any other symptoms?" I asked.

"Well, yeah, I did have a burning feeling in my stomach that moved toward my neck a little. I thought I might even throw up, but I didn't. Maybe it was just some gas, because I did belch a few times. Anyway, I rested, and it's gone now."

Oh, boy. We might have a problem a whole lot bigger than some bad bologna.

"Okay, Bob, I'm concerned. You said you had a burning sensation travel toward your neck. Did you get sweaty? Were you short of breath?"

"You got that right, Doc. I sweat like a horse, but the shortness of breath didn't get very bad."

"And you've been pushing pretty hard to put a wrap on things. Is that right?"

"Yeah, I'm so close to being done, it just made sense," Bob said.

"Bob, have you ever had anything like this happen before?"

"Nope, not that I can think of. I wish I hadn't eaten that bologna—"

"Forget the bologna sandwich, Bob," I interrupted. "Let's go over things one more time. You've been working hard. You ate a sandwich just like you have many times before, but this time you developed some pain in your stomach. It moved up along your breastbone toward your neck, and you were nauseated and sweaty. You were short of breath for a while, but everything's better now. Is that about right?"

Bob replied, "You got it. But like I say, Doc, I think it was the bologna. I think I'll go ahead and finish things up."

"I don't think so, Bob. Your symptoms could be signaling a heart problem, and I'm going to call 9-1-1."

"What! Good grief, Doc. Be serious! It was just some bad bologna. I'm fine now. There's no need for 9-1-1," Bob said and laughed as if to emphasize the ridiculousness of thinking something significant was happening.

"Bob, I'm very serious. I don't think it was the bologna, and I am very concerned. You may well be having a heart attack."

"Well, for heaven's sake, don't call 9-1-1."

It took a few minutes, but Bob and I finally agreed to meet at the local hospital pronto. He was willing to leave my house right away but insisted on driving his own car. I left my office immediately and met him in the emergency room ten minutes later.

An EKG and evaluation were done, and indeed Bob was having a heart attack—his symptoms had nothing to do with any bad bologna. Bob was admitted to the hospital, received an intravenous clot-buster medicine, and did amazingly well as the damage to his heart was minimized. Shortly thereafter an angioplasty procedure (a technique in which a balloon is inflated to dilate blood vessels) reopened the plugged arteries in his heart, and he was back hammering nails in less than a month.

A quarter of a century later, this eighty-year-old friend and patient is still going strong and loving life. The privilege of caring for him ever since the memorable "bad bologna sandwich" has been one of the highlights of my career, and to this day bologna makes me smile.

჈ ჈ ჈

BOB'S STORY GIVES TESTIMONY to a serious warning for patients: when it comes to new or unusual belly pain, don't be in too big a hurry to pass it off as "nothing to worry about." I am thankful my wife did not come home and find a dead carpenter on our living room floor. Patients frequently choose to not investigate puzzling gastrointestinal symptoms because they assume the problem to be indigestion or some other benign ailment. Bob's adamant declaration that bologna was to blame for his symptoms was dangerous. **The inclination to minimize abdominal symptoms may seem harmless but plays a significant role in sudden death due to heart disease.**

჈ ჈ ჈

CALLING BOB IN THE LATE AFTERNOON on that fateful day was a decision I wouldn't ordinarily have made. There were no convenient cell phones clipped to a belt holster in those days, and the interruption of a landline phone call would require Bob to stop what he was doing and walk up a flight of stairs to tell me what I would have learned a couple hours later when I got home. Furthermore, closing time in a family practice clinic is usually chaotic, with last-minute walk-in appointments wreaking havoc with schedules, making an optional phone call to a carpenter unlikely. But that day, for whatever reason, I was sitting at my desk with extra time, and the thought of checking on Bob's progress popped into my head. Why did things play out the way they did? I don't know, but I am willing to consider the possibility that a Divine prompting sparked the notion that calling home would be a good idea. Was it a coincidence or a nudge? I'll let you decide.

But for me, my thought is this: **Casually attributing strange events to mere coincidence may deny me the chance to see the miracles in everyday life, and that would be a pity.**

Pain & AGONY

Pain and agony create motivation

to rotate

the kaleidoscope of life

in search of a new outlook.

THE LAST THING
DAD
TAUGHT ME

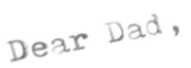

Christmas Day, a time for reflection and a chance to be with family and loved ones, was to be spent at Dad's house, and I knew it would not be dull. With his passion for analysis and discussion, Dad had always been an intellectual hero to me, and he insisted those around him adopt his commitment to lifelong learning. Dad's value system was not complicated: live by the Golden Rule and remember, "to whom much is given, much is expected." Because he had accomplished so much during his life, he was more than ready to encourage his kids to not be satisfied with what they might have already achieved. His typical advice was quite simple: go out in the world and do more. This attitude pretty much guaranteed that a quiet game of cribbage around the fireplace, however nice it might sound, would not be the order of the day. And Christmas that year—well, let's just say it was the beginning of a bleak stretch of time that I could have done without.

"Scott, I think I should maybe see a doctor," Dad commented in an off-the-cuff fashion.

This pronouncement caused me to turn rapidly to face him to ensure I had not misheard. Through the years I had come to regard Dad as virtually allergic to white coats and stethoscopes, and I did not fail to notice he had dropped this bombshell on me when no one else was around.

"What's that you said, Dad? I think I missed something."

Dad smiled and said, "You didn't miss anything. You heard correctly. I've been having some, hmmm . . . some problems with . . . well, I think it's probably a hemorrhoid [a swollen vein near the anus], so I thought I should maybe get it checked out. Can you sort of coordinate things . . . advise me as to what to do?"

"Absolutely, Dad. I'll make arrangements tomorrow and call you before the day is out."

Incredible, absolutely incredible. Did hell just freeze over, or what? Dad is asking me for help, for advice? I can't believe it. He's never asked me for something like this.

I was stunned and a little flattered. On Christmas Day, in a manner of speaking, I had become my dad's doctor. Well, sort of. My thoughts were jumbled.

Dad was an unconditional skeptic when it came to the world of conventional medicine. He was a supremely confident man and often intimidated me. Disappointing him was one of the most dreadful things I could do, and I lived my life trying not to dissatisfy him or give him cause to think less of me. And now he had asked me for help—in the role of a doctor. As far as I knew, Dad had never regarded anyone as "his doctor." As the full impact of his unexpected appeal hit me, I realized I was nervous, and I felt a tension not previously present. It dawned on me how much I wanted to serve him well and have things go smoothly.

Smoothly does not describe what happened.

Two days later, Dad shared with the family that he had colon cancer that had spread to his liver. The cancer was already in the most advanced stage.

Two weeks later, he underwent major surgery. His anus, rectum, and twelve inches of large intestine were removed. A colostomy bag hung from his belly. The removal of waste products from his body would forever be channeled to this man-made depository.

Two months passed with Dad occasionally conferring with me in an "on again, off again" fashion. It was always clear that he was in charge. The nervousness I had experienced on Christmas Day had been a harbinger of what was to come as a minor hemorrhoid concern came to be a mean-spirited monster set on destroying my father's life and terrorizing his mind.

And the monster won.

≥ ≥ ≥

RECOLLECTING AND WRITING THIS STORY has taken me to places I forgot existed. For good or bad, I revisited emotional shadowlands inhabited by villains and heroes, and I couldn't tell who was who. During Dad's illness and suffering, I advocated for decisions to prolong all the high-quality time Dad might have left. He declined my advice and chose death. He threw accusations my way—denunciations of foolishness and selfishness. I buried my anger and sadness and injured pride. I became passive, something new for me. Being vilified by the man I loved and revered was confusing. I hurt for a long time, but I think I am better now.

I told you the facts of his story; now let me tell you the pain of mine.

≥ ≥ ≥

I REMEMBER VIVIDLY the first inkling that Dad might invite death to do its dirty deed prematurely. The two of us were having lunch.

In a quiet voice, Dad uttered words that shook me to my core. "I've been thinking about what the next few months will be like. . . . Realistically, they can only get worse. Right now might be the best I feel ever again . . . and that's pretty darned lousy." He sipped some water and finished his thought. "I'm not so sure I want to go on much longer."

Stunned, I rasped, "Dad, don't give up hope, not yet. You've got some options to consider. You may still have a lot of good days ahead. Radiation therapy could provide some impressive relief. I've seen that many times in my practice."

Silence stretched into awkwardness. My words had collided with a vacuum. I pressed on. "I think, ah . . . I think I speak for all of your children—Dad, we want you with us. We're not ready to go it alone without you."

With suddenness I couldn't have anticipated, Dad's voice cut like a razor. "Don't be naïve, Scott. I don't need some cheerleader's advice. I'm miserable all day long. I don't sleep well. I can't get comfortable. I have cancerous lumps on my anus, and when I sit, they hurt so bad I try to stand as much as I can. The darn cancer is spreading like wildfire, and now I can even feel the tumor masses on my liver pushing up through my abdominal wall." He seemed to tire and was quiet for a few moments before adding somberly, "This disease is relentless. I can't win. So please, let's forego the guilt trips."

Seconds crept by. The shock born of his angry outburst monopolized my thoughts. I waited for the silence to pass. I said nothing.

Finally, Dad said, in an almost conciliatory tone, "Scott, I don't want to go on this way. Waking in the morning is simply opening the door to another day of hell, trying to get comfortable or think about something other than dying. My colostomy bag frustrates me to no end. The adhesive loosens, and then I've got a mess. I live and breathe thinking about my next dose of painkillers; then I worry about the stupid way my mind reacts to the damn drugs. When the day is finally over, I can't fall asleep. I toss and turn trying to ease the pain. This isn't living; this is just dying slowly. I always told myself I wouldn't hang on this way—one day of misery followed by another."

"Okay, I hear you," I whispered.

His words had hit home; they stung. He had ripped into me with a vengeance, and I wasn't interested in being further chastised. I wasn't going to argue, but my mind was churning with thoughts of protest. What had I said that warranted such intense irritation? Was I so wrong to tell him that his kids wanted as much time as possible with him?

He's upset. He's scared. He knows I didn't mean to antagonize him. But he won't invite me back into his private world of thoughts. He won't trust me now that I have openly disagreed with his view that dying soon would be the best thing.

Our luncheon discussion ended. We were both aware that the preceding weeks and months had been navigated with me at his side, and now he was shedding me like a snake sloughs a skin. That day we both lost something precious: unconditional support and mutual respect. We had become guarded with each other.

Dad's consulted me many times the last few months, and I think I've earned the right to speak my piece. Sure, I know the cancer will win, but that doesn't for one moment change the fact that his kids want as much time with him as possible. Lately his questions about dying have changed—they've

moved from casual generalities to specifics. He's looking for detailed informa-
tion about dying: how it will happen, what might speed it along, and—most
importantly—will he recognize when it gets close. His lawyer's mind is build-
ing a case for hastening death, whether through starvation or using strong
medicines carelessly. Something is definitely changing for Dad: he's putting
the focus entirely on his thoughts. He's done talking; he's moved into planning
mode.

Dad had taken the view that death would be a welcome relief and more
life was nothing other than more of the hell he'd already been enduring.

Can I possibly convince Dad that the gift of life is to be celebrated if at all
possible? Can I really ask him to bear more pain, more symptoms, and more
misery?

Ultimately, my questions mattered not.

๑ ๑ ๑

THE NEXT MONTH PASSED by in a blur. Dad lost weight, and whenever I saw
him, it was obvious he was brooding, mulling things over. He quit eating,
predominantly drinking liquids to moisten his throat. He became despon-
dent.

Dad's depressed. Who wouldn't be? I know he won't consult with me any-
more. He doesn't want my advice, and I doubt he would even respect my
opinion if I offered it.

Dad had marginalized me. I was no longer a member of his inner circle.
My usefulness as a doctor with whom he might confer had become a thing
of the past. His rejection cut deep.

I had been fired.

Two weeks later, he was dead. He had given up.

Here was a man who had been a giant among his peers. He was articulate
with a nimble mind; he was logical and discerning; his wit was sharp and his
eloquence formidable. He never stopped urging his children to achieve; he
believed we could always do more. He had served in the state legislature as
representative and senator for a quarter of a century; he had been a leader
whose advice had been sought by fellow legislators on both sides of the aisle;
his career capstone came when he was asked by the governor of Minnesota
to serve as a judge on a state tax court. Only six weeks earlier, we had lunch

and talked and our relationship had splintered. Now he was gone. It seemed incomprehensible.

Our last exchange was two days before his death. He seemed uncomfortable when I asked him for some alone time, away from the rest of the family. I was grateful he granted my request, but I could sense his impatience. One-on-one time with me was not a priority for my lifelong hero. Awkwardly and very self-consciously, I told my dad that I loved him and that I would miss him terribly. Almost grudgingly, he reciprocated in a dutiful manner, "I love you, too, Scott."

I will never know for certain what caused his death, because his widespread cancer had sent fingers of disease in many directions and was systematically shutting down his organs. At my last visit, I knew his body was literally being consumed by the cancer's insatiable appetite. He was a changed man. But I also knew without a doubt that he had given up and wished for death to visit. I'll never know how many days of life were relinquished by Dad's belief that his earthly existence had come to resemble death more than life, but I do know this: **as soon as one makes a concerted effort to expel from the body the spirit of life, it will depart—sooner rather than later—and death will arrive at the doorstep.**

I still yearn to have another lunch with him—not as his doctor, but as his son. I would thrill to know that I was loved by my father in spite of my inability to perceive how difficult his last days had become. I would hope we might confess a shared love—born of blood but also of respect—a love that would last into forever. Regrettably, that won't happen on this side of eternity.

༄ ༄ ༄

In the waning weeks of his life, already grieving, I had sent a letter to my father. A few days later I was visiting him in his home, and he had commented, "Scott, thank you for your thoughtful letter. Some things don't lend themselves to words. Thank you for trying."

And that was that. He made no attempt to elaborate, and his stilted response made it clear that the letter would not be a topic of discussion. When I recently reread the letter, I wondered: *How might things have ended differently?*

Dear Dad,

I am grieving as I begin to digest the fact that some of my expectations for the future are not likely to be borne out. I love you, Dad, and I am not ready to go it alone on this planet without you.

Yesterday in the office, I had a somewhat profound discussion with a patient named Mildred. She has had a life full of hardship, and there is nothing on the horizon to make one believe that her life will suddenly become less painful. Somewhere in the conversation I shared the fact that you have recently been diagnosed with colon cancer, and I indicated that this has had such a profound effect with so much pain. Mildred sort of shook her head and smiled and said, "It doesn't matter whether your dad is 67, 77, or 97, it will always be too soon for him to leave this earth from your point of view."

You indicated last night that you have had the privilege of experiencing sixty-seven happy years, and I agree with you. However, this is happening way too soon. You were real candid, saying that the greatest fear for you is the process of dying. Thank you for your honesty.

Dad, you taught us as youngsters a value system that works. You taught us how to think and analyze and draw appropriate conclusions. You taught us that the highest model of thinking was one based on logic. You taught us the value of integrity and honesty and success.

You have taught me many things, and it now appears that you will teach me another lesson in life. You will teach me how it is that you will deal with the possible conclusion of life, and I have no doubt that I will grow from this experience. I still have difficulty believing that this is happening to us.

Last night Mary [my wife] asked me if I believed in miracles. Yes, I do believe in miracles. Perhaps the greatest miracle I have been associated with is to experience mom's death thirteen years ago, and yet, since then I have had a marvelous opportunity to proceed with my life in an environment whereby you were forever an anchor, a source of strength to be drawn from whenever needed. You have always been there to help if needed, and your love was steadfast. The circumstances surrounding my life the last thirteen years have been really very nurturing, and this is, in large part, due to you. This is one of the greatest miracles that I have personally lived through. So, in response to Mary's question, I do believe in miracles.

Thanks, Dad.

MY FATHER—in living and in dying—taught me many things:

- Dad's cancer was a progressive march to a finish line I knew all too well. I was less than I could have been for Dad when I put my concerns before his. I have come to better understand his bitter words during our lunch conversation. Expressing love may not have been Dad's strong suit, but living authentically was something he did well. I know now that I could have been more sensitive to his plight. Regrettably, **preoccupation with my own feelings hindered my ability to see his pain and fear.**

- Mildred spoke wisely: **"it will always be too soon for him to leave this earth from your point of view."** She was so right: death is always too soon a visitor, and the *when* and the *why* matter little.
- A quote from Bob Marley, reggae music master, intersects well with this story: **"The truth is that everyone's gonna hurt you—you just have to find the ones worth suffering for."** The pain I felt from my dad's piercing words was real, and yet I understand that it doesn't much matter now. What does matter is that Dad is—and always will be—one of those people in my life worth suffering for.
- Living through the ordeal of Dad's cancer and death invited a new appreciation for the orphaned among us. Dad was no longer a mere phone call away; he was unavailable to me. And with this loss, I wanted to cry out to a heedless world: *Haven't you heard? Don't you know? I'm wounded. I'm without a parent on this planet. Don't act like things are normal. They aren't, and they won't ever be again.*

   Despite wishes for a moratorium regarding daily routines, it was not to be. Time trudged on, and all too soon, mundane affairs and humdrum activities dominated my life, and grief was stuffed into a cubbyhole in my brain.
- A life governed by rational thought and logical behavior may have shaped my dad into a gifted analyst, but emotionally he was challenged. He had difficulty connecting with others in the realm of feelings, and his earthly journey was starved for soul food. A complete absence of faith left Dad alone, dreading the prospect of death. I very much wanted to be there for him—to help him if I could—but it was not to be. He died, and I was absent. He suffered, and I couldn't help. Oddly enough, Dad unwittingly taught me one last thing: because a pilgrimage to death's doorstep is a passage pledged to all of us, **I will live mindful that though my body will falter, my soul will travel onward—to a place of which I dream but cannot know.**

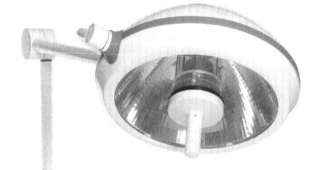

A Doctor
in the Making—
a Work
Never Finished

T he room was a mess, with medical gear strewn everywhere. Catheters and tubes, drapes and stained towels, packaging and needles, oxygen tanks and masks—all combined to create the perfect backdrop for the mood of confusion and sadness the afternoon had produced.

*◦ *◦ *◦

SIXTY MINUTES EARLIER, a delightful fifty-year-old man was in the clutches of confusion and denial when I told him he was having a heart attack. A review of his symptoms during the previous three days along with an exam and electrocardiogram told the story. The medical student working with me had been amazed at Brent's good humor and courteousness—right up to the moment when he stood to walk twenty feet to the procedure room. Suddenly, his body arched into a rigid spasm, and he collapsed into my arms. I gently lowered him to the floor as the medical student stared. She quickly realized he was suffering a cardiac arrest (his heart had stopped pumping blood and death was minutes away), and she elevated his legs and advised a nurse to call 9-1-1.

Over the next hour there was a steady stream of EMTs, policemen, firemen, and paramedics coming and going, providing support however necessary.

I had immediately initiated cardiopulmonary resuscitation (CPR), and after establishing a cycle of compressions and breaths, I glanced over at the medical student, who was wide-eyed and waiting to do whatever needed to be done. I asked her to take over my CPR responsibilities so I could coordinate the overall effort and assist the paramedics with placement of IV lines and preparation for intubation (inserting a breathing tube into the trachea). Without a glitch, the medical student stepped in for me and helped keep Brent on our side of heaven.

The emergency personnel performed flawlessly, gaining access to veins and intubating Brent to insure an airway through which concentrated oxygen flowed. I conferred by phone with ER doctors and cardiologists. Brent was stabilized but remained unconscious.

The ambulance, thirty yards away, broadcast its readiness with screeching sirens, flashing lights, and revving engines. It sped away with its precious cargo while paramedics worked feverishly to strengthen the thread by which Brent clung to life. If surgeons got their chance, a miracle might be in the offing, but the odds weren't good.

✧ ✧ ✧

AN HOUR AFTER BRENT'S COLLAPSE, I looked across my desk at the medical student, who was subdued and quiet. Her large brown eyes revealed shimmering tears pooling at the corners.

We briefly reviewed what had happened, and I said, "He's got a chance, but it's slim. We did what we could; his heart is beating again, and he has pulses in his extremities. The next couple of hours will determine whether he lives, dies, or suffers brain damage."

This young student, stunned but composed, had helped out immensely. Her contributions were real, and she had just endured a sixty-minute crash course in critical care and emergency resuscitation. She would need to process all that had happened. No classroom instruction, Internet video, or textbook could have prepared her for the real-life crisis in which she had just participated.

We sat a few minutes, until I quietly said, "We better go see our scheduled patients. They've been waiting quite a while, so be ready to make a few apologies."

Over the next two hours, some sense of normalcy was restored simply through the repetition of common, everyday activities. An aura of sadness mingled with quiet voices; this combination produced a fragile sense of reality. The medical student carried out her responsibilities and managed patient visits with professionalism and compassion, although her bubbly persona was not apparent.

Later, she and I sorted out some of what had happened, and she said, "It happened so fast. One moment Brent was asking me about medical school, and all of a sudden he was gone, unconscious. I have never seen anything like it. When his heart stopped—it was like an inner force took over his body, making him stiff as a steel beam."

I nodded and listened as she talked. Her emotions were on edge as she described the terror she felt when the prospect of death seemed imminent. I sensed a feeling of inadequacy as she critiqued her own performance.

"If you're feeling as though you could have done better or you should have been able to do more, I can tell you right now—that sense of wanting to be better never goes away. I think it's a big part of what drives us. Physicians take these kinds of emergencies very personally, always wondering what could have been done better or sooner or whatever. Remember this: **the enemy of good is better.** Be a little gentle with yourself; you did a good job. Don't let *better* get in the way of recognizing a job well done."

"Thank you for saying that. That's a good message. Still—I feel so sad for his wife and kids. I know the family, and they're good people. Now their world has

His earthly legacy will not fade easily: a good man, a dear father, a beloved husband, a cheerful friend— all of these identities will be missed.

been turned upside down, and it might never get right side up again." Her lips quivered, and she grew very still.

She had been thrown into a crisis demanding quick responses, and she had accomplished difficult tasks well. She was unaware that seeds of growth had been planted that afternoon that would color her future reactions to emergencies yet to be encountered. The afternoon's drama would change and shape her in ways she could not imagine. Today she had done everything she could to save a life, and she had made a difference.

I considered her worthy efforts and discovered a lump in my throat. This medical student was special to me, and she had revealed that afternoon a glimpse of the doctor she would be—capable and compassionate. I swallowed hard and thanked God. This young woman would care deeply for her patients; she would be there for them, and she would be a gift to her profession. I stepped close and put my arm around her. I thought she might need a hug, and even if she didn't, I did. I was so proud of her: Jackie, the medical student, my daughter.

｜☜ ｜☜ ｜☜

THE PATH A MEDICAL STUDENT will travel is impossible to know. It is filled with hiccups and stops and starts. Time to learn is short, and all too soon clerkships and classrooms give way to electronic health records, quality measures, diagnostic and treatment codes, performance-based reimbursement, insurance exchanges, and the like.

Learning how to be a doctor doesn't occur in a smooth trajectory, because it depends on so many mundane human developments, such as: When will a patient get sick? Where will he go for care? Who will be the medical student in the ER or on the ward to assume his care? Humdrum issues such as these determine a student's daily diet of experiences and profoundly shape a doctor-in-training.

Brent's story reveals a typical example of how a medical student—in a certain place at a certain time—can gain vast knowledge and toughness when least expected.

What else did this experience mean for my daughter? In an odd way, it meant she was beholden to Brent and his family because their pain served her growth. She became a better physician that day and a more wounded human—and both roles are necessary for her to become the doctor she can be. She would never be the same, and on that day she was acquainted firsthand with the disconcerting reality that **the suffering patient serves as a never-ending source of instruction from which doctors continue the ongoing process of learning and growing.**

I guess that's why we "practice medicine." I doubt we ever get it completely right: we just keep on trying.

৵ ৵ ৵

AFTER AN HOUR at the local hospital, Brent was stable enough to be transported to a specialty hospital, where he spent three hours in surgery. The cardiologists worked diligently, trying to open up the blocked artery in his heart, but to no avail. He died five hours after arriving at our office. When Brent checked in with our receptionist, he was conversant and pleasant. In a matter of hours, a single blockage in a single vessel—a "widow maker"—had caused him to leave us.

His earthly legacy will not fade easily: a good man, a dear father, a beloved husband, a cheerful friend—all of these identities will be missed. Serving as his physician has been my blessing, and reaching out to his family will be my honor. I hope the earthly agonies he leaves in his wake will not steal joy for too long. I pray his family can soon see a new dawn breaking and know that Brent is in a place far better than any he has ever known.

The sky grew dark. Night came. My mood was lifeless. Everybody had left. Somehow I couldn't overcome the inertia that held me at my desk. Despite involvement in countless emergencies, I was caught off guard this time. This crisis left me with raw wounds. Brent had arrived in the office and calmly told his story. I advised him of what needed to happen. His response was exactly what mine would have been: he asked for the opportunity to talk it over with his treasured wife. His relaxed demeanor had concealed the turmoil of his body.

His heart attack and death challenged me on a personal level. He was a good friend and several years younger than me. He was a man of honor, possessing guts and humor, and in a world filled with empty promises, he got things done. His gifts were gifts our world needed. Too many people were going to miss him.

I was stunned by the day's catastrophe and knew my grief would not be short lived. Brent's absence would prick my conscience for a long time to come. I was reawakened to the fact that patients not only help doctors grow scientifically, but they regularly remind us of human frailty. Brent's death for me was like being hit in the head with a two-by-four. I couldn't miss the lesson emanating from his death: **life is fragile and uncertain—there can be no taking it for granted.**

And in my time of reflection, I ever so quietly whispered a prayer, one which soothed my soul, albeit just a little:

No man is an island entire of itself;
every man is a piece of the continent, a part of the main.
If a clod be washed away by the sea, Europe is the less,
as well as if a promontory were,
    as well as if a manor of your own were.
Any man's death diminishes me, because I am involved
    in mankind,
and therefore never send to know for whom the bell tolls;
    it tolls for you . . .

JOHN DONNE

Finally, I turned off the lights, shut the door, and went home.

REMEMBER THIS:

THE ENEMY OF GOOD IS BETTER.

DON'T LET *BETTER*

GET IN THE WAY OF RECOGNIZING

A JOB WELL DONE.

SUICIDE VICTIMS
TEACH
FROM THE GRAVE

I'm sorry.

The obituary was nothing special. It reported the facts regarding next of kin and the like. The cause of death was not listed, which was typical.

I thought about my last visit with Clara, and guilt wormed its way into my consciousness as I recalled our conversation.

"You seem sad, Clara. Is there anything going on?"

"Not really. Nothing special. I'm tired. Good grief, I think I've been tired my whole life. Dr. Jensen, you know Clem isn't doing well. Even thinking about being in a nursing home will be the death of him. And we don't get along well. He's grouchy, says little, and does even less. And I don't make much of an effort anymore. It's hardly what I'd call a marriage. We're roommates at best, but we can't afford to live in separate homes. You know Bill, don't ya? Our son? He just can't seem to get over his divorce, and he drinks too much. If I say anything, it just makes things worse. Oh, I'm sorry, Doc. I don't mean to dump all this on your lap."

We chatted about many things, and Clara was matter-of-fact about her life and its trials. Her mood was gloomy and contagious. Every word she uttered was soaked with sadness. I tried to assure her that she was not burdening me and that I was there to listen. When I suggested she might be suffering from depression and maybe I could help, she smiled sorrowfully and no longer seemed interested in talking. I asked her to call me if I could be of any assistance.

Clara's really hurting. I wish I could break through her tough exterior. I hope she's willing to reach out if things become overwhelming.

"I'll let you know if I need you. I've been working on arrangements, and one of our neighbors might be able to help us out enough to keep Clem at home. He needs to be lifted and bathed, and I can't do it anymore. Nothing is easy these days, but what the heck: that's life, I suppose. I do know this, Doctor—nothing happening in my world will be solved by any pills or shrinks."

I missed my chance. There they were: hints littered the field of our last conversation:

"Good grief, I think I've been tired my whole life."
"We're roommates at best, but we can't afford to live in separate homes."
"I can't do it anymore."
"Nothing happening in my world will be solved by any pills or shrinks."

She had put all her ducks in order. And I didn't catch it. I missed what was happening.

I can't believe Clara really did it.

The facts were pretty straightforward, and the cause of death was established without any fuss—suicide. When the coroner called me, he described his interview with her son, Bill, who said that Clara had recently been complaining about feeling old and was ready to call it quits.

Wow, to simply walk into a river, lay your body down on the muddy bottom, and wait for the suffocating water to fill your lungs and end your life—pretty damn incredible! But that's the way the coroner put it together. I wonder how she fought off the body's natural buoyancy? I hope it all went quickly.

Sadness enveloped me. Clem might stay home for the time being, but he would fare poorly. Regardless of how estranged the two of them had become, he would miss her, more than he realized. More than she would have guessed.

No details were released to the public. The family hoped the circumstances of her death would not come to be widely known, and they weren't. My personal sadness surrounding Clara's death was magnified by my inability to perceive her intentions at our last visit. Everything about her departure was unsettling and incomplete.

In the ensuing weeks and months, any public interest in this seventy-five-year-old woman's death dissipated uneventfully. But grief lingered for me. And I didn't know why. It didn't evaporate like some water-based mist. It kept welling up to capture my heart all over again with an unpredictable wondering about the *whys* and *hows*. While the mystery and distress accompanying Clara's exit almost drove Clem and Bill crazy, I simply sat at my desk more often than usual, wallowing in maudlin reflections. I wouldn't have expected to be so captivated by the death of this remarkably determined woman.

⁂

"DOCTOR, we need you here—now! Suicide attempt. Ambulance en route!"

Jim had hung himself with a self-made noose and had dangled from garage rafters while partygoers reveled in the adjoining house. Fortunately, his slowly twirling body was discovered within minutes, and 9-1-1 was called immediately. The merriment ended abruptly, and the attendees quietly vanished into the night. The paramedics arrived with lights flashing and everybody ready to roll. Cardiopulmonary resuscitation (CPR) was initiated on site, and the ambulance quickly transported Jim into my life.

The frigid wintry night heated up quickly. Regrettably, it took only a few minutes in the ER with my newest patient to establish a diagnosis. My initial inspection revealed unsurprising bruises shadowing purple on his neck—the rope had been strong and done its work well. His face was flushed and puffy—obvious signs born of strangulation. The eerie bulging of his eyeballs gave the impression that he was staring at me, and the dilated red veins coursing over the "whites" of his eyes evoked sympathy for the misery he must have suffered when the rope was first called on to hold his weight.

The WHY *distracts us and tethers us to the dying moment.*

But the key findings came from the neurologic exam that revealed that Jim no longer responded to any pain stimulus—prodding his cornea with a needle or twisting the flesh of his chest into a knot provided no reaction whatsoever. Other procedures and tests were conducted and demonstrated conclusively that Jim was dead; that is to say, brain-dead. This was the diagnosis that dictated what would happen in the ensuing hours.

I quietly but purposefully declared that Jim was dead, and the nurse recorded the official time of pronouncement. Then everything changed. Efforts shifted course and preparations were made for a "human harvest." The irreplaceable and ongoing CPR efforts sustained Jim's organs despite the fact that his brain—the critical center of human existence—had already succumbed.

A sequence of actions that might seem gruesome to some became life changing for others. Despite never speaking a word to Jim, the single goal of sustaining the vitality of his tissues monopolized my time and efforts through the wee hours of the morn. Phone calls were made, police were asked to locate family members, forms were faxed, administrators were notified, and the university hospital transplant team was mobilized.

For more than three hours, heroic efforts continued on Jim's behalf—more correctly, on his body's behalf. During this time I learned that Jim was single, and his father had been located on the other side of the state—which made a grim situation worse. Jim's dad could not get to the hospital to say good-bye. In the midst of tears and from a distance that spanned more than mere miles, a father gave permission for organ and tissue donation. I thanked him for the gifts that truly would never stop giving. It saddened me to know this father's excruciating journey of grief was only just beginning.

Meanwhile, the emergency crew and I toiled on in a surrealistic fashion: ten thousand chest compressions and two thousand breaths were the necessary ingredients to keep Jim's body alive. His brain had already completed its dance with death, and his body would soon be allowed to do the same once his final surgery was completed.

Harvest—what an odd way to describe Jim's sacrificial contribution to mankind. A crop of tissues was to be secured and dispersed to others. The harvest team arrived to conduct its ghoulish exercise in the retrieval of lungs, kidneys, heart, corneas, blood, bone marrow, skin, and the like. My job was finished—tissue oxygenation had been maintained, and I signed off. The soft-spoken members of the surgical crew took over, and I never even learned exactly what was taken. I was confident Jim's final gifts would bring life-giving hope to many yet-to-be notified recipients still participating in their travels on planet earth.

In the ensuing weeks and months, recollections of Jim glided away from my active consciousness, only to lurch back into my thoughts without any warning. And then I remembered: grief doesn't evaporate like some water-based mist. It keeps welling up to capture my heart all over again with an unpredictable wondering about the *whys* and *hows*. I never even met the guy, so I wouldn't have expected to be so captivated by the death of this remarkably determined man.

ʝə ʝə ʝə

AFTER A HARD DAY'S WORK overheating its customers, the blistering sun was finally giving way to twilight. I stepped out of the quiet emergency room to get a breath of air untarnished by the antiseptic smells of a hospital and was greeted by an oppressive blanket of heat, heavy and quiet. It seemed that even the bullfrogs had been too scorched to contribute their usual noises. While an occasional cricket broke the silence, the songs of birds were completely absent, and I wondered if the towering gray cumulonimbus clouds gathering in the west held ominous tidings of things to come. Yes, a storm was a distinct possibility, and who knew when it would strike.

"Doc, we need you, and we need you now!" squawked the excited nurse's voice over the radio clipped to my belt. Moving quickly back inside the confines of the hospital, I was advised that multiple car crash victims were en route. Confusion at the site had necessitated that two emergency vehicles be dispatched, and when I heard their fast-approaching sirens, I felt the familiar release of adrenaline surge into my veins. The foreshadowed storm I had pondered had shown itself, not in the skies, but in my emergency room.

The ambulances cornered sharply into the emergency garage, and it was evident that the situation in the field had been challenging as the paramedics in the first vehicle rushed a youngish woman, a middle-aged lady, and two small children into the trauma bay. The crew from the second ambulance moved more slowly as they attempted to inconspicuously transport a gurney carrying a black body bag down the back corridor that led to the morgue.

A subdued but intense mood permeated the ER as the staff efficiently moved into high gear assessing the injured and obtaining pertinent medical facts. We learned that a suicide attempt had been successful, and that the deceased would patiently await the tools of the pathologist. The forty-five-year-old victim would not require my skills, since she had been pronounced dead in the field from high-velocity blunt trauma rupturing multiple organs. Judy jumped from a pedestrian bridge that arched over a four-lane freeway, and her timing was such that she landed on a sedan driven by a woman with three passengers—her two children and her mom. Judy's body shattered the windshield into a thousand diamonds of glass and dropped into the front seat. From there it violently bounced off the driver and her mother, careening into the back seat where it settled on the laps of two toddlers, unlucky kids who likely were recent kindergarten graduates.

The next hour found me intently concentrating on my four new patients, and I was grateful to find no significant physical injuries. I relied on the social services counselor to address the emotional trauma and make arrangements for necessary counseling referrals. What had begun as a mellow night in the ER ended as a "downer" for all as we brooded over a life that had—by choice—inexplicably ended.

In the ensuing weeks and months, recollections of the surviving family members diminished. But memories of Judy did not. I was sure she never intended to horrify two small children, but her leap from a walk-over bridge did just that.

I thought of her often, and I didn't know why. And then I remembered: grief doesn't evaporate like some water-based mist. It keeps welling up to capture my heart all over again with an unpredictable wondering about the *whys* and *hows*. I never even saw Judy's face, so I wouldn't have expected to be so captivated by the death of this remarkably determined woman.

࿄ ࿄ ࿄

SUICIDE IS NO STRANGER to me, and when it visits, a common question is often not far behind: "How did the victim's anguished perspective of the world go so wrong?" This question is seldom answered with any satisfaction, and guilt surrounding the death lingers like a smothering fog.

Grief arising from suicidal death is not reconciled by trying to solve the mystery of *why* the victim chose an early exit from life. The reality is this: the *why* distracts us and tethers us to the dying moment. If the victim's life is to be given its due, we have to give up that quest. Passage of time will grant plenty of opportunities to analyze the enigmatic question of *why*, but eventually such occasions may wear out their welcome. Clara drowned leaving no note, Jim hung himself without warning, and Judy's leap was devoid of clues. In none of these tragedies were we given to know the *why*.

Suicide yields its secrets grudgingly. Standing silently and letting raw wounds sting as they must will more likely bear fruit—sometime, someway, somehow. Regardless of how much effort and determination are brought to bear on the question of *why*, answers will be elusive, and my counsel is this: **celebrate the pieces of the victim's life that allow for rejoicing and embrace these memories often.**

Suicide victims teach from the grave. We can acknowledge their agony and empathize with their torment even while we endure our own lasting confusion and sorrow. Release from that which hurts us—guilt, loss, separation, regret—is not found easily, but the lingering pain can teach us. I have learned that grief is calmed when I reach out to disconnected people in my own sphere of influence. If I can extend a kind word or a helping hand and assist injured souls to view this planet as a tolerable place, my efforts can make a real difference, not only for the wounded but also for me. **Compassion extended to others has an odd way of coming full circle, helping to heal even the most obstinate of wounds, especially the ones that keep welling up to capture my heart all over again with an unpredictable wondering about the *whys* and *hows*.**

She Deserved Better

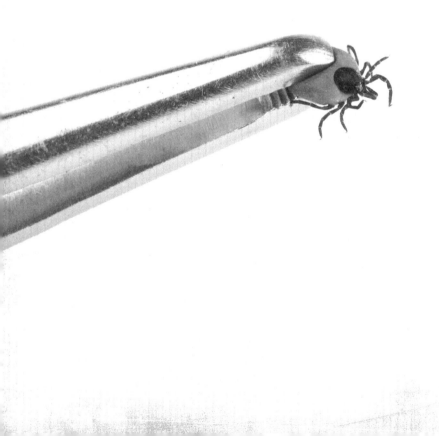

*S*aying *"I don't know" would have been honest and a lot less belittling. I wish the doctor had used those words instead of the ill-fated verbiage he selected. Laura's hurting, and from her description of the ER visit, I can't blame her.*

"I feel so worthless and helpless. I don't understand why so many of the doctors I see think I willingly choose to collapse and fall to the ground hard enough to get bruises all over my body—that's ridiculous! I've visited the emergency room half a dozen times in the last couple months and been admitted to four different hospitals. I hate this, I really do. Dr. Jensen, is there no help? I don't understand why my heart isn't working properly. Why can't doctors fix this?"

"Doctors don't have the answer for a lot of problems, Laura. I understand your frustration, but I don't know what to tell you," I said, desperately wishing I had something to offer. I didn't.

"And when the ER doctor told me he thought it was stress related and I should see a counselor, I about blew a gasket. What am I supposed to take away from a comment like that—that I'm some kind of nut?"

And then the tears came. Her eyes shimmered, and big drops rolled down her cheeks. Her makeup smeared, and her face publicized her hopelessness.

She deserves better. It's enough to endure this ordeal, but my colleagues have unwittingly made things all the worse with their implications that what she suffers from is in her head. It's no wonder she's exasperated. When she needed compassion, she got nothing but insinuations that the problem was of her own making. She's not going to trust anyone in a white coat for at least a while, and that's sad.

A day earlier I had contacted the cardiologist on call and reviewed Laura's situation, and he had astonished me when he said, "Scott, I'm very familiar with Laura's case because I've seen her a couple of times in the ER when I was asked to consult. I think the problem is in her head, and she might benefit from seeing a psychiatrist. Her symptoms and exam sure don't match up with anything I know of. She probably needs to find a different way to deal with stress. Who knows? Maybe counseling will help."

I was disappointed by my colleague's flip attitude and also a little angry, but I swallowed my frustration, knowing his words were simply his way of confessing he had no answers.

I hated telling Laura that I could offer no solution, but I did just that. I suggested a consultation at a medical center specializing in diagnosis and research of heart problems, but I was disappointed in myself for not being able to contribute something more.

So Laura made yet another appointment with yet another doctor, someone she had never met who would ask the same questions she had answered more than a dozen times. She would go filled with a spirit of dread, lacking hope because already so many healers had labeled her as damaged goods suffering from something "in her head."

Her spirit might have been nourished rather than terrorized had she heard the words "I don't know" instead of feeling branded as, in her words, a "nut case." She deserved better.

ƀ ƀ ƀ

Laura's experience lays bare a nasty and ugly habit doctors have developed over the last several decades. By overlooking the impact we have on the human spirit, we have demonstrated all too often a willingness to consign perplexing patient concerns to the catchall diagnostic term: *in your head*. This cop-out is particularly tragic when patients come to us suffering and confused and leave not just without answers but with bruised self-esteem and confusion regarding which direction to turn.

The phrase *in your head* holds the power to accuse and condemn with a speed and thoroughness so overwhelming that patients frequently withdraw from any further attempts to seek help, choosing instead to live with their demons. Doctors can—with a paucity of words—banish any hope of a solution and even cause patients to blame themselves for the disorder from which they suffer.

Patients need to step away from the doctor visits and the hopelessness and **remember just how limited physicians were only a couple generations ago in understanding, diagnosing, and treating the vast majority of ailments afflicting mankind.** Only in the last century have antibiotics, sterile surgical procedures, and vaccines become part of a doctor's armamentarium with which to fight disease. Who knows? Tomorrow may reveal answers for today's mysterious ailments and grant doctors one more tool with which to heal the sick and the suffering. Meanwhile, patients must appreciate that current-day medical knowledge has very real limitations, and doctors need to appreciate how their demeanor and words affect patients.

Patients must appreciate that current-day medical knowledge has very real limitations.

Let's step back and consider a tale of supposedly overexcited mothers in a place called New England.

In the early 1970s, many parents in Lyme, Connecticut, were unnerved over the plight of their children enduring puzzling symptoms, including swollen knees, rashes, headaches, weakness, and chronic fatigue. Doctor visits and hospitalizations proved unproductive, and some parents were even cautioned to pay less attention to their children's growing pains and more attention to their kids' behavior problems. Were it not for the tenacity of a couple of especially strong-willed mothers who challenged the local medical professionals via diligent note taking and research and persistent phone calls, Lyme disease might yet today be regarded as nothing more than a collection of harmless symptoms.

These mothers—who refused to accept their doctors' assertions that what ailed their children was *in the head* or else mere growing pains—ultimately pushed their concerns past these patronizing physicians and finally obtained an audience with the Connecticut State Health Department. Researchers were persuaded to investigate, and by 1975 a description of a new disease involving joint pains, rashes, headaches, and a causative bacterium had emerged—and Lyme disease was born.

❧ ❧ ❧

Complicated patients

might be better served

if doctors more often confessed,

"I don't know."

DOCTORS ARE TRAINED TO EITHER know the answer or to find the answer. When efforts to know or discover the answer are not met with success, physicians are inclined to judge a solution-less problem to be neither a lack of knowledge on their part nor a gap in scientific understanding. The comfortable presumption favors an explanation outside the realm of actual organic disease, most likely having something to do with stress or "mental issues," and a favored expression is this: "It's not organic, so it must be functional." Pity the patient labeled with a "functional disorder," because help is not likely on the way. While such assumptions may allow the doctor to more comfortably move on to the next patient or task, these labels hold the power to terrorize patients and initiate cycles of frustration, self-blame, and resignation.

Complicated patients might be better served if doctors more often confessed, "I don't know," but doctors often find the task of admitting ignorance awkward and embarrassing. They may forego the opportunity to exhibit compassion or advocacy and in so doing disregard the opportunity to contribute to a trust-based relationship. Frustration is not an emotion exclusive to patients, and when doctors are faced with "not knowing," they may abandon the "art of medicine" and carelessly use words to cast blame anywhere but on their own shortcomings.

Patients: don't be too willing to accept as gospel truth all that the doctor claims. Remember the children of Lyme, Connecticut. The problem wasn't *in anyone's head*—it just took some time to realize the nature of the issue and find a solution. You are not a nut case, but your problem may be ahead of its time, and until medical science "catches up" with your ailment, you are especially vulnerable. Trust your instincts, do some homework, and be willing to consider alternative approaches. What have you got to lose?

THE PAIN OF INADEQUACY

"Dr. Jensen, I don't think Father Noah is doing well, so be prepared. I think he might be losing it," my nurse told me.

"What do you mean, 'losing it'? What's up?" I asked.

"Oh, you know how he gets when he's stressed—hyper and hard to understand. Today he's fretting about the world we live in and angry that people fly airplanes into buildings. Nothing made much sense, and he just kept rambling on, so I told him you would be in shortly."

"All right. Thanks for the heads-up."

I sure hope Father Noah is okay. He gets worked up sometimes, and I know he's been under a lot of stress.

"Hi, Noah. How are things going these days?"

"How can you even ask, Doc? Good grief! Some days this world gets me so riled up. Airplanes exploding into the Twin Towers in New York: my head is spinning. Why can't humans just get along?"

Huh, what's he talking about? He's fidgety—that's for sure—and obviously agitated. Maybe he heard some bits and pieces of tragic news and got things a little mixed up. Noah's always been a little inclined to exaggerate. I doubt there's any substance to his claim.

I excused myself, informing Noah I needed to retrieve a blood pressure cuff. Once out of earshot, I asked the receptionist to turn on the radio. It was nine o'clock in the morning, and I hadn't listened to any news since the night before. I thought I better double-check on Noah's comments before assuming he was off base and confronting him with concerns about his emotional stability.

Within a few seconds, the radio newscaster was recapping a dramatic and unbelievable event. A tragedy in New York City soon to be known simply as "9/11" had just occurred, and the world would never be the same:

> Two planes hit the Twin Towers of the World Trade Center—large passenger jets. Both towers are in flames! The Pentagon may also have been hit. An explosion in rural Pennsylvania has just been reported. America is under attack! . . . Oh, no! One of the towers is shaking—both are shaking! Heaven help us. The South Tower is collapsing. It's buckling! It's crashing to the earth. People are jumping from the building! God help us. Thousands of people work in those towers.

A marathon of horrors had begun. Soon the North Tower would crumble. Americans would know without a doubt that the jihad of the terrorists had reached the shores of the United States.

What the heck! Father Noah isn't losing it—he's simply overwhelmed by something immensely overwhelming.

I returned to Father Noah and completed an exam and reviewed some lab results. We expressed our sorrow and confusion about the appalling attack in New York City. I was glad I had asked the receptionist to check for a news report before assuming Father Noah had some sort of mental problem. His agonizing outpouring of words had nothing to do with delusions. Nine-eleven may have seemed otherworldly, but painfully we were learning—moment by moment—just how real it was.

Thinking our visit was over, I stood up to leave, but Noah wasn't finished.

"Doc, I don't understand this. This is just wrong. This is evil! Thousands are dead, missing, or maimed. And for what? Because some terrorist on the other side of the globe strikes out against America because he chooses to believe in a religion of hate? This makes no sense, Doc, no sense at all. What can I do? What can you do? What can any of us do?"

Silence filled the air, and finally I said in a whispered submission, "I don't know, Father. I wish I did, but I just don't know."

"That's just it, Doc! None of us knows, and that's not okay. This world is spinning out of control, and I can't deal with it anymore! I don't know if I even want to be a part of this world. Can't you help me get my arms around this—at least a little?"

"Noah, I'm sorry. I just don't know. I don't know how to make sense of any of this."

In the midst of my inadequacy, our visit was finished.

❧ ❧ ❧

A LONG TIME AFTER the debris of the Twin Towers had been scooped away, and even after the mastermind of that terrible day had been dispatched, I discovered words that eased my lingering pain brought on by 9/11. Unfortunately, I did not have these words for Father Noah on that day of enduring sadness. All I could offer him was silence—evidence of my disappointing inadequacy—and three feeble words, "I don't know." But I am thankful that I did finally stumble upon cleansing words of submission that now provide me consolation through the simple acknowledgment of my humanness. I am most appreciative of the essay "Discipline and Other Sermons," by Charles Kingsley:

> Many things puzzle me; and the more I learn, the less I find I really know: but I shall know as much as is good for me. . . . And for the rest, puzzled though I be, shall I not trust Him who . . . made this world?

On a bright and sunny September morn—when our country was collectively filled with anguish and desperation—Noah's plea for a salve for his wounds struck a painful blow to a physician trained to avoid the words "I don't know." Nine-eleven was a day of destruction for all of America, but for me personally it was a day my heart was pierced by a devoted priest who asked me to soothe his pain. I could not help him—not even a little. I had no remedy for his despair. I gave him no consolation.

More than a decade passed before I was touched by the surrendering words of Charles Kingsley: "puzzled though I be, shall I not trust Him who . . . made this world?" **A simple trust in something beyond the human realm revealed a way for my soul to make peace with the challenging words "I don't know,"** and this gave me the release for which I had been searching ever since my disappointing acknowledgment, "Noah, I'm sorry. I just don't know."

There are no answers
to some of life's issues,
and we need to admit that.
But a simple trust in something
beyond the human realm
can reveal a way for our souls
to make peace with the challenging words
"I don't know."

GRIEF
UNRESOLVED

I arrived home a little before midnight after a full evening of meetings, and my wife, Mary, looked at me with concern and said, "I think you better call the emergency room right away. I got home just a little while ago, and the ER nurse already called twice. She wouldn't tell me anything but said she's been trying to get ahold of you for hours."

"Okay, thanks. I'm not on call tonight, so I didn't carry my beeper. Maybe I should have. Oh well, I'll give them a call."

After I called the local hospital, circumstances were anything but clear.

"What's up?" Mary asked.

"I'm not sure. I spoke with Dr. Glavin in the ER. He thanked me for calling but then told me he had no information other than I was supposed to call the county hospital morgue. He didn't know anything else but said the county hospital had asked for some help in locating me. Something's happened, but I'm not sure what. I would guess it's about a patient, and it doesn't sound good."

And so it began. I made several calls and was finally connected to someone in the morgue—a man named Chester.

"Chester, this is Dr. Scott Jensen. I understand you want to talk to me about something."

"Oh, Dr. Jensen, yes, I've been trying to reach you. I'm the technician on duty and so glad to hear from you."

What's he talking about? It's midnight, I've never met him, and he's telling me how pleased he is that I called. What's this all about?

He continued, "I apologize for the late hour, and I'm sure you're wondering what's going on. We have an unidentified body here in our morgue, and there's a possible connection to you. I've been instructed to ask you to call the police for details. I'm sorry to sound so mysterious, but I'm not allowed to say anything more. You should ask for Officer Brady, and the number is 612-666-1111. Perhaps you would be so kind as to call me after you speak with him, because we would appreciate any help you can give in establishing the identity of our John Doe."

So there it is. Someone is dead, maybe a patient of mine. I don't know who, how, when, where, or why. I better get to the bottom of this.

I called Officer Brady and advised him of my conversation with Chester. Officer Brady launched into a quasi-interrogation about my background, but I really wasn't in the mood.

"Officer, could I suggest you simply tell me what's going on? It's midnight."

Officer Brady took no apparent offense at my gruffness and seemed to appreciate my no-nonsense approach. Without a trace of emotion, he outlined the facts point by point that were contained in a police report generated in the preceding seven hours.

"Dr. Jensen, at 5:05 this afternoon, the metropolitan police received an emergency call from a patron staying at the Madison Hotel on the 494 freeway. He said he saw a man climb onto a chair on a small balcony at the Premier Hotel about three hundred yards south of him, on the other side of the freeway. He watched the man climb up onto the railing of the balcony, which was located on the top floor of the hotel. He saw the man teeter for a couple moments and then jump, doing a sort of swan dive. The man saw nothing else of note. His view of the grounds of the Premier Hotel was obscured by a couple rows of pine trees. He saw no one else on any of the other balconies. As far as he could tell, he was the only witness to what had happened. He was incredulous and called 9-1-1. I took the call, and he told me his story.

"A squad was dispatched. The officer at the scene went first to the check-in desk at the Premier Hotel, and no one there knew of anything out of the ordinary. But when the officer went to the north side of the hotel facing the Madison Hotel and explored the area, he discovered a male lying face up on the loading dock with obvious deformities of both legs. The victim was not breathing and had no pulse. No significant blood pools were seen, and no evidence of any struggle or foul play was identified. An ambulance was dispatched to the scene, and because the deceased carried no identification, he was classified as a John Doe and transported to the county hospital morgue."

I interrupted Officer Brady. "That was seven hours ago. Have you learned his name?"

"No, we haven't, Dr. Jensen. By seven o'clock the pathologist at the county hospital had completed a preliminary exam of the body that revealed the following: Caucasian John Doe, approximately thirty years of age, weight of 140 pounds, seventy inches tall, slender build, and extensive closed head injuries with multiple extremity fractures. The presumed cause of death is a closed head injury secondary to a jump from the eighteenth floor. Lab and toxicology studies are pending. No identification was present on the body other than a white slip of paper, two inches by two inches, in the right front pocket of his blue jeans. The piece of paper had the name *Scott Jensen* and the phone number 952-442-0000 printed in black ink on one side, and the other side was blank. Now that I have spoken with you, I can cross you off the list of possibilities."

What in the world is going on? Were the police thinking I might be the dead John Doe? Who committed suicide? Do I have any patients who have recently been unstable? Why would my name and phone number be the only information found on this dead guy?

... Oh no, no, no! It couldn't be. No, it couldn't. Don't even think it, Scott.

The officer continued on with his report, but I sensed an ominous distraction pulling at my brain. I had to work at concentrating on what he was saying.

"By 8 pm the police investigator assigned to the case completed his report. At the Premier Hotel, he questioned the manager and the desk clerk about our John Doe. The manager checked all the eighteenth-story rooms and found one that contained a newspaper on the bed and a couple of coins on the desk. This room revealed no toiletries, no clothes, and no luggage. The location of the room coincided with the location of the body discovered by the dispatched officer at around 5:30 pm. The desk clerk had checked in a slender young Caucasian male around 4 pm. The patron had paid his bill of forty-nine dollars and fifty cents with cash—small bills and change—and signed in as Jim Smith. The address was illegible, and no ID was seen or requested."

Officer Brady finished up his report by telling me that the voice message at my home phone number, 952-442-0000, had provided him with the information that Scott Jensen was a doctor, so he called numerous local hospitals. This was how he learned that I was on the medical staff at Ridgeview Hospital and worked in the emergency room and also at a clinic in Watertown.

"That brings you current on the matter, Dr. Jensen. We have not received any missing person inquiries tonight, and there was no evidence of any foul play. Now we have eliminated you as a possibility for the John Doe, but that still leaves us without a name and not much to go on. You might be able to clear up the identity issue by visiting the morgue. John Doe may be a patient or acquaintance of yours; he probably knows you, and you might recognize him. I'm not sure of the status of the body or recognizable features. You will have to work out the logistics with the county hospital. I think that's the next step," Officer Brady concluded.

I shuddered as my mind raced.

Could it really be possible? Should I give voice to my suspicion? I better. I might feel like a fool in a few hours, but I need to share what might be significant.

The concerns expressed earlier in the evening by both Dr. Glavin at Ridgeview and Chester at the county hospital made sense now—they were relieved I wasn't dead! My hands were clammy and nausea twisted my stomach. My throat tightened, but I went ahead and divulged my fearful thoughts.

"Officer Brady, I have a younger brother, Bruce, who recently turned thirty. He's had some mental health issues and is living in a halfway house. I don't know the name of it, and I don't have a phone number. When my dad died a few years ago, he entrusted Bruce's health care to me. I have been in charge of his medical issues, but my older brother is his legal guardian. Bruce may not be connected with any of this, but the possibility does exist. I'll call the morgue and work out the details of what I should do. Thanks so much for your efforts. We'll be in touch."

The next few hours passed in a kind of trance. Ultimately, I drove down to the morgue in the wee hours of the morning, and in the hot, formaldehyde-ridden confines of an elevator cab, I examined the body of a thirty-year-old John Doe, dead about twelve hours. My vision melted into a watery prism.

Mr. John Doe was bruised, broken, and crumpled, and he was my brother.

And I was broken, too. Bruce was gone. Tears slowly trailed down my cheeks.

My brother, Bruce, with his history of mental and emotional problems, had obviously been suffering more than I had realized. A month earlier I had taken him to a movie, and we laughed and drank soda and ate popcorn. A week earlier he spent the day with our older brother, who had called me and said, "Bruce and I had a good time on the boat today. He was in good form and enjoyed himself."

"Good form" for someone on the edge might mean his "searching" was nearly over—that decisions had been made. How could I not have seen that something was changing? I've been his doctor for the last few years, and we got together almost monthly.

I felt a smothering fear come over me as I realized Bruce was gone, really gone. I couldn't grasp this new reality. I couldn't shake the feeling that I should have seen this coming.

I cringed as I thought about dropping eighteen stories in a few seconds and wondered what passed through Bruce's mind as he neared the earth. I wrestled with many questions: Why did he jump from hundreds of feet up knowing that he would have to endure a significant duration of time—agonizing time—to fall to his destiny? Did he choose this method so that he couldn't change his mind and couldn't fail? Was he running from some demon that wouldn't leave him alone? Could I have somehow done something to prevent this?

As I stood alone in the elevator cab with my hand cradling the cheek of my little brother, an odd thought came to mind. *Had Bruce rushed to death like a child rushes to the outstretched arms of a parent?*

Time may

ease the pain,

but it won't

replace

the part of you

that died

when your

loved one

departed.

❧ ❧ ❧

QUESTIONS MATERIALIZE EASILY from any suicide, but answers aren't so forthcoming. In my grief, a paraphrased verse from the philosopher Horace accused me: "if a man looks with love and compassion on his suffering fellow man, and inquires of God, 'Why do you afflict my brothers?' then surely this man is gazed upon more tenderly by God than a second man who applauds God for the mercies which allow the second man to flourish happily. For the first man questions God out of love and pity for his brother, attributes regarded highly by God, but the second man speaks out of selfish complacency, a beastly trait which does not please the spirit of God."

Do I own the guilt of the second man? When I spent time with Bruce, was I focused on his real needs, or was I guilty of just going through the motions because my own life was good and I was content? Was I a little too impressed with myself for sacrificing my precious time to be with Bruce?

I shuddered that these questions even took form in my mind. Did their mere presence convict me of the very sin I feared? I felt like the verdict "guilty as charged" had already been decided.

In the aftermath of his death, I searched for answers. While I hoped for comfort and absolution, I found nothing but an unappeasable thirst. My quest became a painful journey through the troubled landscape of my mind.

I had to admit that even during our best get-togethers, Bruce and I struggled to communicate. Heartbreakingly, I had to accept the reality that our status as brothers was based more in name than in love.

His death forced another obligation onto me as well: it poked and prodded me to reexamine unfinished business from earlier family deaths. His exit seemed to demand, for whatever reason, that I learn something more about the essential nature of grief, something I had not come to grips with previously. This directive drove me back in time and ushered me into emotional places I did not want to visit. This ordeal proved to be long and excruciating. It proceeds still.

≈ ≈ ≈

I WAS RAISED in a small Midwestern community surrounded by a nurturing family in a time when the notion "it takes a village to raise a child" enjoyed broad agreement. My mom was my best friend, my dad was my hero, and my siblings were good to me. Bruce, the baby of the family, was seven years younger than me, and though we didn't play much together, we were affectionate with each other and seldom fought. While my childhood days were idyllic, lessons in heartache soon stormed into my life—all too soon and all too often. Mom died in her forties from colon cancer; Dad died in his sixties from colon cancer. Multiple aunts and uncles died from cancer far before the age of Medicare eligibility, and teenage cousins committed suicide. Several school friends were killed or maimed in bicycle accidents, and a couple more drowned. By the time I reached my twenty-first birthday, I was already highly skilled at stuffing grief into a cubbyhole where it could be controlled and do little damage.

When Bruce's suicide jarred my world, grief raised its ugly head as never before. When I looked down on the bruised, broken, and crumpled body of my brother, a smothering blanket of awareness came over me, and I felt a bone-deep fear that I was no longer in control. No more would I be able to dodge what grief required—it demanded my complete attention and would settle for nothing less.

Old scars were peeled away against my will. I was overwhelmed. Grief had become an indomitable force, and this time around it was relentless. A war raged within. I sought closure, but found only new layers of empty, gnawing pain. Dredging up the deaths of Mom and Dad—and so many others—gave rise to a fury brewing in my heart. I struggled mightily. My emotions were fragile and paper thin. Tears came often, sorrow was my daily shadow, and the emotional roller coaster I rode was unstoppable.

Trivial encounters—a friend shaking my hand, a casual expression of affection, two brothers enjoying a baseball game—produced a lump in my throat so intense I could barely speak. When routine daily activities were too prominent in my thoughts, guilt would hound me because I had not remained mindful of Bruce's death and suffering. I couldn't stabilize my feelings. I was a mess.

I desperately wanted to regain control of my life—but wanting something didn't make it happen. Inner peace was not simply elusive; it was an impossibility. I prayed hard, but prayer didn't settle the matter. Friends told me time would heal and encouraged me to let go of Bruce's death. But grief refused to cooperate. I wasn't able to let go of the thought of Bruce's misery; I was haunted by Mom's consuming malignancy; I relived Dad's cancer-induced exit.

My spirit was fractured. Fun wasn't fun, sleep wasn't restful, and demanding that my wife read my mind when I was as broken as Humpty Dumpty was happening a whole lot more than it should.

Hollow inside and feeling worthless because I couldn't manage this life crisis, I decided to try a different approach. Out of sheer frustration and hopelessness, I chose to deliberately challenge grief by increasing contact with this demon. I embraced circumstances that were likely to involve death or anguish. I didn't attend just a wake or a funeral—I attended both. I made house calls to help with deathbed needs. I saw nursing home patients after clinic hours just to hold their hands while they slid toward God's side of eternity. I made it a habit to stop at the scene of auto accidents to see if the emergency responders needed any assistance, and I assisted in triage situations and pronounced accident victims dead on the scene.

Slowly I came to appreciate that **my pain lessened when I involved myself with the pain of others.** My experience mirrored that of George Bailey in the movie *It's a Wonderful Life,* when his personal anguish was relieved by reaching out to save his fellow man—Clarence drowning in the river. George's decision to respond to Clarence's need paralleled my own resolution to run toward—not away from—the grief of others. For me, and perhaps George, too, this choice had the effect of taking the first dose of penicillin for pneumonia—I started getting better.

I continued to welcome encounters with grief into my life, and my patients cooperated by providing a steady stream of illness and ailments that granted me ongoing opportunity to come alongside them in their own struggles with sadness. Grief became a steady companion and familiarity nullified its weapon of surprise: **though I couldn't avoid grief, I could render it less crippling by expecting it.**

Time plowed onward, and slowly the weight of sadness lifted—just a little. I came to realize that grief was not the furious enemy I had made it out to be. It was more like a thief in the night than a cataclysmic event. It occurred randomly but not uncommonly. It was always lurking around the next bend, always waiting, and ambushed me when least expected. When its sharp pain receded into the shadows of my life, I knew we would meet again. **Grief was not a hiccup of life; it was a part of life.**

So it was that after my brother's death, my decision to confront both current and stored grief slowly bore fruit. **The balm for my wound contained three ingredients: be involved with the grief of others, expect grief to show its face often, and accept grief as an inescapable part of life.**

With this awareness, peace knocked on the door of my heart, and I let it in.

৯ ৯ ৯

A QUARTER OF A CENTURY has passed since the jump from the eighteenth floor. I don't know the *why* for Bruce's action. I know he did it, and I really don't think I could've stopped it—and that's about all I know. There was no suicide note, but I'm glad to know he enjoyed a good day boating a week before his death. However it happened, a scale was tipped, and life as a gift became subordinate to the beckoning of death. His demons cannibalized their host, but he was able to finally escape their hold. No longer would he have to endure; with death he could embrace the unknown.

A final teaching, one wrought from my own heart: **time may ease the pain, but it won't replace the part of you that died when your loved one departed.** Your broken heart will heal. A scar will form. That part of your heart forever is changed, and its passions and joys will always be a bit muted. That's simply an undeniable reality arising from lost love—lost because someone left.

When the bighearted Robin Williams left, his premature exit signaled an end to the laughter and passion he used to touch so many. The pain of his departure will not yield easily to the mere passage of time. Yes, scars will form—but scars can't feel. The heart's capacity to feel joy is lessened when a part of it dies and twists itself into a knotty clump of fibrous tissue. Robin Williams's death had enormous impact because his influence was widespread, but on a cosmic scale his exit was no different than any other. **All suicides leave in their wake scars that can't feel joy and lost loves that can't be retrieved.**

Transitions

Transition, however awkward,

however unsettling,

*grants to the eaglet—*FLIGHT,

*gives to the butterfly—*WINGS,

*bequeaths to the human—*GROWTH.

Face of Aging—
Gratitude and Grace

"You know, Doc, I still have the urge."

I looked at my eighty-year-old patient quizzically and replied rather loudly, "Are you having problems?"

"Well, yeah, I haven't done it in years."

At this juncture, I was a bit perplexed because Liam and his wife were both in their ninth decade of life, and evidently there had been a hiatus in the kind of activity he was referring to. Wilma was only five feet away from her husband, obviously hearing his comments. She said nothing, but from the corner of my eye I saw her intently monitoring our exchange.

Pausing, choosing my words ever so carefully, I asked, "Hmmm . . . Is there something you would like me to do to help?"

Liam tersely responded, "Yeah, get me a medical clearance for my pilot's license. Damn FAA won't let me fly because of my hearing. My hearing is just fine. And I sure do have the urge to get back up in my plane."

I breathed a sigh of relief and almost laughed out loud as it slowly dawned on me that Liam wasn't about to ask for samples of the blue pill, i.e., Viagra. He had been referring to his strong desire to get back in the cockpit and do what he loved. His pilot's license had been revoked a while back because he couldn't pass his medical exam due to profound hearing loss. Liam knew full well there was nothing I could do to reverse his medical grounding and probably suspected that I was in full agreement with the FAA. Quite simply, he was almost deaf.

But I understood his desire to get back in the saddle to do some takeoffs and landings. I had been flying for over twenty years and had experienced a similar longing anytime I had been away from the pilot's seat for more than a few weeks. But that didn't change anything for Liam: he was grounded and grounded for good. His piloting days were over.

Even though I can't help Liam with his pilot's license, I'm glad he felt comfortable venting his frustration with me. He can be a little crotchety, and it would be nice if Wilma could be spared a few of his never-ending complaints about the FAA.

I glanced at Wilma to see if she had appreciated the misunderstanding stemming from Liam's comment about urges. The hint of a grin made it clear she had been aware of my confusion. Amusingly, she seemed content to say nothing, instead merely enjoying the moment—even if I hadn't.

≥ ≥ ≥

THE CHALLENGE OF MAKING concessions to the aging process is tricky. The gift of an extended life span carries with it the frustrating reality that diminishing capabilities may dictate giving up certain joys or passions. And worse yet, the need for transitioning defies predictability. The odds go against us with each passing year.

The dilemma of growing older is further aggravated by the mismatch of reduced skills with ever-increasing rules and regulations involved with common activities or hobbies such as driving, flying, fishing, or hunting.

What strategies might help Liam deal with his age-related trials and allow him to adjust without anger or bitterness?

Let me tell you of a patient who against all odds succeeded in navigating the treacherous road of aging and disability. She is a spirit-filled woman who humbly and unknowingly touches the hearts of many. Through her I witnessed the essence of successful transitioning to a "new normal."

Daisy, a seventy-year-old delight, somehow developed the ability to smile in the face of severe and deforming arthritis and casually comment, "Oh well, this body is just about used up anyhow." Before she became home-bound, her childlike enthusiasm for each new day granted her favored status at our clinic. She was adored and appreciated, and her seize-the-day attitude invigorated all of us.

Daisy is something else. How does she do it? How does she endure a life filled with pain and hardship and still smile, laugh, and shower grace and gratitude on everyone she meets?

One fine summer day sitting at her bedside, I simply asked her, "Daisy, how do you do it? How can you give such powerful testimony to grace and gratitude when life has robbed you of the chance to do so many of the things most of us take for granted?"

What she revealed was a gift, a kernel of wisdom lying in wait for all of us.

"Dr. Jensen, I grew up in a time when fire and brimstone were the reality of the day. God was presented as an angry cosmic bully holding threats over our heads if our behaviors were not according to the law of the church. But for whatever reason, during my formative years I adopted a different view; I don't know how or why. I saw my Creator as full of grace and mercy and love. Armed with this view of God, I saw life through a different lens than my family or friends. To me, it seemed natural to focus on God's grace when things were tough. In a different way, but sort of similar, it also seemed logical to be grateful when life was good."

"How old were you when the rheumatoid arthritis hit, Daisy?"

"Oh, let's see. I was young, barely twenty. I was lucky that grace and gratitude had already been touching my soul for some time. When I was told by the doctor that I had arthritis, how could I have known that it would take only a few years for this disease to rob me of my mobility and afflict me with never-ending pain? Thankfully, grace and gratitude were already daily companions: they saved my life."

"When you realized the arthritis was crippling you, how did you respond?"

"Oh, I got mad, that's for sure," Daisy said with an easy smile. "I kicked and fought some. But it didn't take long for me to realize that this horrendous disease wasn't going to be any kinder just because I was angry. So I had to step back and try to find another way to look at my struggle. I chose to envision grace and gratitude as angels fighting for me against the devilish arthritis."

"That's inspiring, Daisy. Do you have any advice I can share with patients who are having a hard time accepting their 'new normal' state of reduced capabilities?"

"Well, maybe. You know, Doctor, it makes no sense to get in a tug-of-war with a chronic disease or growing old. **Learn to say, 'it is what it is,'** and try to chuckle, at least a little. Recognizing the reality of the day releases me from a lot of what-ifs and motivates me to make the most of whatever life can give. For me, saying 'it is what it is' isn't an apathetic giving up; it's more a kick in the butt to acknowledge the way things are and then go and do what I can."

"That makes sense," I said.

"I also think it's important to search for things to be thankful for. Every morning I try to count my blessings—a loving God, caring family and friends, the warmth of the sun, a cool breeze, or even the sound of rain on the roof—and these joys invite a grace-filled feeling into my heart. I like myself better when I'm in a mood to appreciate things. Nothing good comes from dwelling on pain or stiff joints. I'm convinced we'd all be better off if we could **learn how to be grateful when things are good and how to be graceful when things are not so good."**

"I think you're right about that, Daisy."

And my house call was over.

⁄◌ ⁄◌ ⁄◌

Daisy had learned a secret: **our decisions shape who we are and who we become.** The more we choose something, the more we become that something. Our lives form our identities by the decisions we make. Each choice we make provides a momentum in the direction of making more similar choices. What begins as a single decision can snowball into a powerful force determining who we will become.

Daisy touched me that day with her commitment to a life filled with grace and gratitude, and she reminded me of three laws of love taught in the church I attend. **1. See others as God sees them. 2. Do unto others as you would have them do unto you. 3. Love others as God loves you.**

And if I find myself in danger of forgetting about grace and gratitude, I reflect on this favorite parable, "Two Wolves."

> One evening an old Cherokee told his grandson
>   about a battle that goes on inside people.
> He said, "My son, the battle is between two wolves
>   inside us all.
> "One is evil. It is anger, envy, jealousy, false pride, greed,
>   arrogance, self-pity, guilt, resentment, inferiority, lies,
>   superiority, and ego.
> "The other is good. It is joy, peace, love, hope, serenity,
>   humility, kindness, benevolence, empathy, generosity,
>   truth, compassion, and faith."
> The grandson thought about it for a minute and then
>   asked the grandfather, "Which wolf wins?"
> The old Cherokee simply replied, "The one you feed."

◁ ◁ ◁

THE STORY OF A frustrated pilot characterizes well the face of aging with its inevitable physical deterioration. Given time, no one eludes the reality of years zipping by and the concessions demanded therein. Father Time can be ruthless and is certainly tireless. I still chuckle when I recall the comment of a patient nearing the age of seventy: "I thought it would take longer to get old."

As for me, when "growing old" demands more than I think it should, I try to reminisce about people who lived, regardless of accumulated years, with grace and gratitude as their companions. Then I smile and recall that their wisdom was often born simply by deciding in advance "which wolf would be fed." And then I smile even more, realizing just how many of these souls were patients I had been blessed to serve.

HE DID IT
HIS WAY

A cold wind blew across the front yard of the funeral home as I stepped out of my car to attend the wake of my patient and friend, Sam. He had lived a hard life, sometimes just scraping by, but always accepting responsibility for his actions. He had enjoyed hunting and fishing immensely, and his daily routine always included a couple packs of Camel cigarettes and at least one thermos of stiff black coffee. A handful of Sam's favorite chocolate malted milk balls topped off a singularly unhealthy lifestyle. During his early forties, he had gained twenty-five pounds, launching him past the two-hundred-pound mark, and his blood pressure rose right along with his weight.

I reflected on Sam's usual response when I would offer advice about ways to enhance his health. "Come on, Doc, my pop and granddad both died early from the big one [a massive heart attack], and I doubt I'll be any different. So what the hell, let's not get too hung up on these life changes or whatever you call 'em. I'll do as I do, you do as you do, and we'll take what comes. By the way, did I tell you about that huge mother of a bass I hooked last month? Damn, it was close to a record in the Guinness book!"

Walk the walk,

don't just

talk the talk.

Sam would then regale me with stories of his most recent adventures with his teenage boys and completely ignore my recommendations regarding a healthier lifestyle. So it came as no great surprise when his wife called to tell me he had been found dead in his hunting shack. The coroner in northern Minnesota had signed the death certificate, so I was out of the loop regarding any details. I worried about this close-knit family losing a forty-five-year-old father and husband, so I made arrangements to attend the wake, hoping to connect with them in their time of grief.

Once inside the funeral home, I quietly stepped up to the registrar, signed my name, and picked up an announcement that summarized the more public aspects of Sam's time on earth but included little of his private life. I smiled when I read the part about his love for hunting and fishing and how time with his family, especially his boys, was his favorite pastime. The queue to pay last respects to Sam slowly crept forward, pulling me along with it. I was thankful that the ambient noise level, while subdued, contained lots of chatter with occasional chuckles. Intrusions of weeping and wailing were far less than I had anticipated in light of the tragic prematurity of his death. I tried to compose some thoughts to share with his wife and kids, but first I wanted to have a chance to contemplate prayerfully over the coffin.

When the space in front of the casket cleared, I stepped forward and glanced down. I almost gasped aloud when I saw what lay before me.

What the devil? Is this some kind of joke?

The open casket displayed Sam's body in a fine fashion with a true resemblance showing forth. But it was obvious the mortician had not called the shots for this wake, for here was Sam with a super-sized package of chocolate-coated malted milk balls sticking out of the left breast pocket of his flannel shirt. And my eyes fell on the right breast pocket of his shirt, which only partially concealed a pack of protruding Camel cigarettes. And there, grasped in his hands—why not?—was a silver flask used for the occasional nip while waiting for the deer to move or the fish to bite. The laying out of Sam's body was anything but typical, and I grinned in spite of myself and the surroundings.

Soft whispers behind me disrupted my reverie, and I gazed one last time on Sam's face, feeling both sad for his departure and grateful for his life and our relationship. My eyes blurred with tears, so I elected to stay put, stay quiet, and stay in the moment as I said a silent prayer:

God, here lies Sam, my friend, and I ask you to gather his soul into your embrace. He is a good and honest man who lived his life as he thought he ought.

I moved to embrace his wife and shake the hands of his teenage sons. Emotions welled within, allowing only a whispered voice as I shared these words: "I'm sorry for your loss. Sam knew who he was and didn't snivel or whine about why he didn't have this or that. Without shame he owned his actions, good or bad and regardless of outcome. He is a good man, and I have been privileged to be his doctor and his friend. I pray with confidence that God blesses Sam and each of you."

When I walked out the front door, the wintry gale didn't seem so frigid, and my soul was at peace. Best darned wake I'd been to in a long time.

᠔ ᠔ ᠔

DRIVING BACK to the office, reflections of prior visitations flooded my mind.

A lot of wakes and funerals have little to do with reality. They're filled with platitudes, confused theologies, and unrealistic notions about the misfortune of death. I remember the funeral for Adolph, a mean old man who routinely drove his children to tears with cruel guilt trips. He couldn't die soon enough for them, but still, his eulogy was filled with absurd comments about his tender spirit, and as soon as his family had finished parading to the pulpit to share a few insincere tales of a charitable life, they snuck out to the parking lot for a few shots of brandy. I still cringe when I recall Adolph's final farewell. So great was the deception that I had to double-check the funeral bulletin to be certain I wasn't at the wrong church.

Sam's wake was an entirely different kind of affair. It was a recognition of the values he lived by and an invitation to acknowledge the man he was. By pulling no punches, his family had honored his choices.

When Frank Sinatra made famous a song about a self-made man "facing the final curtain," the words "I did it my way" touched the hearts of many. Sam's life gave witness to the words of this song through a spirit of confession, conceding a stubborn self-reliance but never forgetting the majesty of his Maker's creation. He cherished his independence and owned his mistakes, but he also thanked God for the life he'd been given. He lived and died carrying few regrets, and I remember still his refreshing style of telling me where to get off when I advised him of my latest and greatest plans to help him get healthy. His legacy was simple and to the point: **walk the walk, don't just talk the talk.**

Sam's wake reminded me of the importance of authenticity, especially during our final good-bye. I was touched by his farewell in a way I could not have expected.

❧ ❧ ❧

Relationships between physicians and patients continually evolve, and I am often perplexed by a haunting sense that I need my patients just as much as they need me. When a cherished patient passes on, I weep for the loss of a friend, the loss of a patient, and the loss of a teacher. Such sorrow is not only okay, it's restorative; the sadness that grips me in such times is therapeutic. **Mourning is a powerful catalyst for transformation. Past transgressions, emotional scars, and lasting resentments—all sorts of painful memories—get scrubbed clean, and then "letting go" can happen, opening the door for the gift of renewal to work its magic.**

Mourning is a powerful catalyst

for transformation.

Past transgressions, emotional scars,

and lasting resentments—

all sorts of painful memories—

get scrubbed clean,

and then "letting go" can happen,

opening the door for the gift of renewal

to work its magic.

Too Much Sanity
May Be
Madness

Anice-looking young man in his early twenties sat in the exam room with hands folded in his lap. He seemed nervous, and staring at his feet allowed him to avoid eye contact. I introduced myself and asked how I could help.

"Well, this will sound stupid, but I have these thoughts. They . . . they . . . well, like they pester me. They won't leave me alone. They go round and round in my head, and I can't get rid of them. They are making it hard for me to get my work done at school, and my grades are slipping. I didn't know what to do, so here I am. I was wondering if you could help me."

Over the next few minutes I asked a lot of questions and did a brief exam. Taylor seemed like a normal college student—likeable and candid. I zeroed in on the thoughts that were troubling him.

"Taylor, I think I can help, but can you tell me a little more about these thoughts?"

"Doc, I can't get things off my mind. I get stuck . . . on a thought. Sometimes my brain seems to insist that I reread a sentence even though I have already read it three times, and I can't ignore the goofy command. I reread the darn sentence one more time and still get nothing out of it. Then I get bummed out that I gave in to the weird impulse, and I wonder what's wrong with me. . . . And it's not just with reading that I get stuck. If I'm doing a math assignment, sometimes I get trapped on a problem, and I'll repeat the calculations even though I solved it right the first time. One part of my brain is screaming, 'Get going, you have a lot of work to do!' And another part is saying, 'Oh no, you don't. You have to recheck that subtraction one more time.' Then I get stuck; I redo the subtraction until it 'feels right.' It makes me want to scream!"

Taylor was getting a little riled, so I interjected, "Taylor, you're doing a good job of describing how these thoughts intrude on your thinking. This makes it easier for me to understand what's going on—"

"Doc, it gets worse!" Taylor interrupted. "I'm good at math, I really am, but these thoughts slow me down so much, I don't even finish some of the exams because I run out of time. On the midterm test, I didn't even get a chance to look at the last five problems because the bell rang, and I had to hand in my answer sheet. I've been so frustrated that I decided I had to talk to someone. Am I going crazy?"

I paused before saying, "No, you are not crazy, not at all. If it makes you feel any better, I see patients every week with concerns similar to yours. You're describing a typical obsession—you get stuck on something, and even though it makes no sense to the logical part of your brain, you somehow feel obligated, even forced, to give it its due. An obsession is an unwanted and repetitive thought that won't go away."

Taylor looked a bit confused and said, "You mean this kind of goofiness is common? I've never heard of an 'obsession,' but it sure sounds like what I have. Why haven't I heard about these things?"

"Taylor, do you really think people are going to discuss their obsessions openly? People are pretty closemouthed when it comes to talking about their quirks or how weird they think they might be."

I went on to explain that sometimes obsessions lead to compulsions, which are physical acts aimed at satisfying the obsessions. Compulsions come in many forms—tapping a finger, swinging a leg, muttering, resetting an alarm clock four times, rechecking the locked front door, nibbling the lip till it bleeds, and even rereading a sentence over and over. They can overwhelm and control the otherwise rational mind with an iron grip.

"Doc, I was worried sick and thought I might be going crazy. I was even feeling depressed. Maybe I'm getting more worked up than I need to. You make me feel a whole lot better, and I'm sort of amazed how you understand what's going on in my head."

"Obsessions are a big deal because they can be so commanding and irresistible. Make no mistake about it: retraining your brain to ignore an obsession is no easy task."

I had Taylor complete a couple surveys helpful in the diagnosis of depression or a mood disorder. When he was finished with them, I analyzed the results.

"Taylor, you're having obsessive thoughts, and they're obviously creating issues for you. I don't find any evidence for depression or mood disturbance. You're not weird or crazy. But obsessions are devilishly persistent and can lead to full-blown anxiety or depression syndromes, and I don't want that happening."

"So, can you help me?" Taylor asked. "My schoolwork and grades are really important to me, and they're the things that pushed me to finally see you. This is a huge deal for me."

"Yes, I believe I can help you, Taylor, and I think a medication will play an important role in our overall strategy." He was paying close attention, so I continued, "I want you to understand that being obsessive is like a two-edged sword—something that can offer both good and bad consequences. You have to train your brain to seize the good aspects and overcome the negative ones. I think you can be successful in this, and if you're willing, I can prescribe a pill to help."

Should I discuss my own quirks? How deep do I want to go in sharing with Taylor? Oh, what the heck. He'll probably benefit from hearing a reality story, and it might just help him turn his obsessive tendencies into a positive force in his life.

"Normal is a setting on a washing machine but has little to do with humans."

"Taylor, doctors are some of the most obsessive people I know, and I'm in that group. I am very obsessive and have many compulsions that, embarrassingly enough, I routinely carry out. I have spent a lifetime learning to manage these habits and turn them to my benefit, but still I fail miserably at times. Sometimes I daydream about what it would be like to be easygoing, with a devil-may-care attitude. Realistically, that's not going to happen, so I've had to learn to live with who I am. Even though I can see a lot of positives stemming from being super-conscientious about details, I get very frustrated with myself when that same thoroughness tips over into the area of being just plain obsessive."

Taylor slowly nodded his head and said, "Doc, you don't know how much better that makes me feel. If someone like you struggles, I guess I can be a little easier on myself."

"I think you should be a little kinder to yourself," I quickly replied. "Remember, being a little obsessive can actually be helpful. If you can harness or control your inclination to get fixated on things, you may end up developing high-level skills in areas that require strong detail orientation."

Then I paused, searching for the right words. "The most important thing you need to remember for now is that you're as normal as you need to be, and the concerns you've shared with me are qualms many people experience. *Normal* is a setting on a washing machine but has little to do with humans. Five hundred years ago, Miguel de Cervantes wrote, 'too much sanity may be madness,' and I agree with him wholeheartedly."

Taylor chuckled. "Nobody ever told me it's okay to be a little strange. Thanks, Doc. What you say makes sense, and if you think I could benefit from a medicine, I'm game."

"Okay, but let's also try this: the next time your mind is insisting that you have to think or do this or that, try to step back and marvel at the incredible way your brain works. Welcome the goofy thoughts as a part of your individuality, and don't be in such a hurry to kick them out of your head. Smile and say to yourself, 'Yeah, I'm a little quirky, a little weird, but that's me.' Celebrate your uniqueness."

He nodded. "I've always tried hard to drive these disturbing thoughts out of my mind. I never thought to welcome them in and just smile at myself. It's worth a try."

"Taylor, we'll work together. For now, make peace with yourself and how you think. It's okay to let bothersome thoughts exist—they are what they are. You don't have to eliminate them; just recognize them as the silly and spontaneous outpourings of a typical brain. Try as you might, you can't control everything produced by your mind. It really is okay to ignore the bizarre ideas that pop up in your head and simply move on. Concern yourself with thoughts that arise from your own active consideration and view them in the context of your knowledge, experience, desires, hopes, and dreams. I think you'll find more inner peace, and you may develop the ability to chuckle at yourself. Let your brain be the awesome blessing it is. Let thinking be a joy and not a curse, and remember this: you're as normal as normal can be, and now that you have exposed these quirky obsessions for what they are, you don't have to be afraid of them anymore."

I gave Taylor a prescription and asked him to return in a month.

⋇ ⋇ ⋇

AT HIS FOLLOW-UP VISIT, Taylor told me he had noticed significant improvement with his obsessions. He definitely seemed more at peace with himself and the world around him. Our conversation was spontaneous and sprinkled with quiet laughter. A couple months later I received a letter from Taylor. Here are some excerpts:

Dr. Jensen,

For years now, I've been seeing doctors and telling them all my symptoms about anxiety. I always felt like just another patient on just another day.

You have no idea how happy and fortunate I feel having come to you. I really just want to thank you for helping me and guiding me through this difficult and confusing time. You've done more for me in two visits than ten years at other doctors' offices. I now have confidence I'll get through this.

Thank you.

Taylor

THERE IS SIMPLY NO SUBSTITUTE
FOR A HEART-TO-HEART DISCUSSION
BEFORE ANY PRESCRIPTIONS ARE WRITTEN.

MOST PATIENTS SUFFER from one mental health issue or another at some time in their life. One of the greatest obstacles preventing doctors from understanding and helping these patients is lack of time. Conversations regarding emotional or mental health concerns do not lend themselves to quick and easy explanations. Patients commonly harbor a fear that prescription drugs will alter their personality, which makes successful intervention even more difficult. **There is simply no substitute for a heart-to-heart discussion before any prescriptions are written.**

I advised Taylor that I think we're all a bit crazy, and we discussed the elusiveness of being "normal." We talked about the likely outcome from a trial of medication. The extra time spent with Taylor at the front end of this challenging issue helped accomplish three key tasks necessary for his improvement: **1. his troubling issues were discussed candidly, 2. his uniqueness was positively reaffirmed, and 3. the idea of anyone truly being "normal" was exposed as an impossibility.**

Taylor's letter reaffirmed the value of going the extra mile for patients, especially when dealing with sensitive mental and emotional health issues. It made all the difference for him. Reassurance can move a patient's attitude from denial to hopeful. I have been gratified to see many patients gain an internal peace by confronting their peculiarities and declaring, **"I may not be normal, but I'm close enough; and being normal is probably overrated."**

As Taylor said of his quirks, "I've always tried hard to drive these disturbing thoughts out of my mind. I never thought to welcome them in and just smile at myself." We would all do well to hope for such graceful acceptance of our own uniqueness.

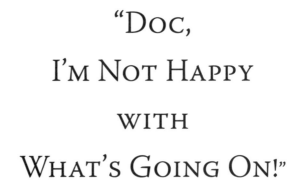

"Doc,
I'm Not Happy
with
What's Going On!"

To Dr. Jensen,

I wanted to let you know my views on electronic medical records (EMR). If your clinic goes to this type of recordkeeping, I will change doctors and clinics. We are told that the records will be safe, but nothing is safe in the world of computers.

The hacking of systems has never been so high. The best of the best are being hacked. So don't tell me EMR is 100 percent safe; that's a flat-out lie.

In a day of the Privacy Act, I have never felt so violated by people trying to get into my personal life.

Concerned, Larry

THE LETTER BREATHED ANGER, but I understood Larry's annoyance. Larry made his living selling insurance products, including health insurance, and he knew what was happening with privacy violations in the industry. He was skeptical of the truth of many government pledges, and his fears regarding consumer protection with EMRs were eminently reasonable as several large hospital and clinic EMR systems had recently been hacked into, with thousands of personal medical records becoming potential fare for Internet consumption. His views were consistent with a public plea by Dr. G. Keith Smith in an article in the July 7, 2014, edition of *The New American*: "The electronic medical record (EMR) is basically the federal government's way of getting your medical records, and you [losing] your confidential relationship with your physician."

Larry's correspondence was not a complete surprise because he had been remarkably opinionated during a physical exam two months earlier. I recalled our conversation easily:

"Dr. Jensen," Larry warned, "if your clinic goes to an electronic medical record, my family and I will have to leave you. That's hard for me to say because you've taken good care of us for a quarter century, and you were always there for my folks. I trust you, and you know the medical history of my family inside and out. But my family won't go to a clinic with an EMR."

"Larry, my colleagues and I have no intention of using an EMR."

He relaxed a bit, uncrossing his arms. "I got a letter from my insurance company wanting to know why I wasn't taking my medicines regularly. I told the lady to go to hell. I told her I'll deal with my doctor when it comes to the pills I take. I am sick and tired of insurance companies and the government sticking their nose in my business. Doc, I'm not happy with what's going on! I can't imagine how you tolerate this interference."

He has no idea just how much meddling I put up with! If he only knew that when his insurance company claims to be concerned for the quality of care he receives, there is usually an underlying agenda to which he will not be privy. I don't have the time to explain that "quality" is a nebulous term referring only to aspects of medical care lending themselves to measurement. The real "stuff" of healing is not some item that can be dissected, quantified, and put in a board report.

"I hear you loud and clear, Larry, and I appreciate your candor."

"Insurance and government plans should stay out of our business. I can figure out what works for me, and if I can't, I'll call you. I don't think these bureaucrats give a hoot about their customers. They want dollars and control and the heck with our relationship. Good grief, you're my doctor, not them; you're the one I trust—they don't know me or even care about what I want."

Strong words, but I understand his frustration.

Larry went on to share a few more sentiments, some of which reminded me of a *Minneapolis Star Tribune* article (September 25, 2014) by David Goldhill: "Since Medicare's inception, government and health insurers have tried to control health-care prices; fifty years later, it's time to admit failure.... We need a solution tailored to our reality. Let's reduce the role of the big intermediaries . . . and increase that of the one force that can drive good behavior: the consumer."

When Larry started to get heated up again, I broke in and said, "Larry, I appreciate your interest and concern, I really do. We need more people thinking and talking about our health care system because we're at a tipping point. The patient-doctor relationship has been compromised by many of the so-called advances in health care delivery: EMR, computers, automated phone menus, and even the Internet. All of these influences weaken the bond that has traditionally served the patient and doctor very effectively. Even the insurance companies have gotten into the act of routinely under-cutting our relationship. Things have gotten pretty impersonal these days."

"You hit the nail on the head, Doc!" Larry exclaimed, throwing his hands up in the air. "That's exactly what's wrong with health care today! The personal touch is disappearing. I hear that from a lot of my clients, and some of them feel as though they have no control regarding their own health. What do you think the answer is?"

"In my mind, **patients need to be in charge of their own health, and doctors need to be patient advocates. It's as simple as that.**"

I had other patients to see, so we concluded our talk.

᠁ ᠁ ᠁

WHEN I RECEIVED LARRY'S LETTER a couple months later, I suspected he would appreciate a reply, so I wrote him the following:

> Dear Larry,
>
> I wanted to respond to your concerns regarding electronic medical records and also elaborate a bit on a few topics we have discussed in the office at different times. You and I have enjoyed candid and broad-based discussions for years, and I thank you for that.
>
> We both know the last fifty years have brought about dramatic changes in the health care scene. Medicare started in the 1960s, HMOs in the 1970s, and from there things changed pretty quickly. Unfortunately, one of the casualties of these government and insurance intrusions has been a long-standing pillar of health

care, the patient-physician bond. This relationship has suffered many insults, and the cumulative effect has been to render it far less potent than in the past. **Direct communication between patient and physician has always provided me with the best information to solve and treat people's ailments.**

The onslaught of technology has invaded the patient-doctor bond as computer interfaces, electronic medical records, and automated phone menus have gutted many of the personal qualities of patient care. Today the patient in need no longer determines his need, and the giver of care no longer determines the care to be given—our system of caring doesn't convey a feeling of compassion.

I think the last stronghold of support for patients and doctors is one another: together we need to define what we think is most important.

Your concerns regarding the electronic medical records (EMR) are well founded. The recent commitment to an EMR by Medicare and insurance companies is confounding in so many ways. **The EMR is no friend of efficiency or compassionate care. It tends to dehumanize the caring involved in the patient-doctor relationship.** Many studies have demonstrated that the essential ingredient of face-to-face contact between patient and doctor has been significantly reduced by the interference of the ever-present computer screen. EMR proponents promise enhanced quality of care, reduced expenses, more engaged patients, and reduced medication errors. These pledges have not been realized in any significant way. It's safe to say the EMR experiment has cost American taxpayers billions of dollars, and in most situations patient access to care has actually decreased.

EMR does accomplish one thing quite well. It allows the government and insurance companies much greater ease in tracking patient behaviors and habits. That capability is a little frightening.

During one of your office visits, you mentioned your frustration with your insurance company because they contacted you directly regarding the medicines you were supposed to be taking. I don't blame you for being irritated, and I want you to understand that I firmly believe you are the person in charge of the pills you take. You and your insurance carrier can communicate directly, but if any changes are made in your medication plan, please let me know so I can update your chart. Thanks again for the stimulating conversation and the privilege to be involved in your care.

Sincerely,
Dr. Scott Jensen

⁂ ⁂ ⁂

DR. RICHARD MORRIS summed up well the thoughts of many physicians regarding the confusing and unwarranted government endorsement of electronic medical records (*Minneapolis Star Tribune,* March 26, 2015): "Why is government so set on this [EMR] mandate? Because it wants to mine the data for public health information. But for the physicians who have to use these [EMR] systems every day, who judge their (EMR) potential on patient needs rather than pleasing Big Brother, the negatives at present are too great." In the same essay, he also commented on privacy breaches due to hacking resulting in intimate psychological and financial data becoming available far and wide for discovery and misuse. His willingness to address these issues so candidly has been an encouragement for many physicians as they struggle with what to tell patients such as Larry.

I routinely remind patients that they possess both common sense and a good understanding of their own needs and wants. **Their input is important, and our health care system will be the loser if their voices are not heard. Patients and physicians, working together, make a formidable team, and both benefit from mutual trust and advocacy.**

A Soldier's
Toughest Battle

*C*OURAGE is almost a contradiction in terms. A soldier surrounded by enemies— if he is to cut his way out—needs to combine a strong desire for living with a strange carelessness about dying. He must not merely cling to life, for then he will be a coward, and will not escape. He must not merely wait for death, for then he will be a suicide, and will not escape. He must seek his life in a spirit of furious indifference to it; he must desire life like water and yet drink death like wine.

From *Orthodoxy* by G. K. Chesterton

PTSD: Post-Traumatic Stress Disorder. What is it? Is it simply a manufactured psychological term describing stress-based issues that follow some type of intense physical or emotional trauma?

No, that's not it—not at all. PTSD is a whole lot more than some letters conjured up to designate an anxiety problem. PTSD is a demon without flesh; it derives shape through relentless mental and emotional torment; it feeds on self-hatred, and its favorite victims suffer from doubt, confusion, or unresolved fear. It causes frailty and never shows mercy. PTSD is a monster that can be as large as the universe.

⁊⊚ ⁊⊚ ⁊⊚

THE SOLDIER SENSED a pursuit. He was being pursued, but nothing more was clear. His race from the unknown pursuer was without end, so he knew he could not prevail—that was certain; he could feel it in his bones. But he dared not give up because then he would be as nothing or—even worse—he would be a coward, and he knew the pain of that already. And this internal terror was a secret his mother could never know.

Lately something was different. The chase was picking up speed, and no waking hours were left untouched. His only respite occurred when he was distracted by the need to assist his mom, helping her endure end-of-life suffering and seeing to it that she could die with dignity. But this labor of love would not require his efforts much longer.

≥ ≥ ≥

SHE WAS OLD. Actually, she was very old. Ninety was not far off, and she looked a lot older than that.

"I am good for nothing, Doc. Can't ya help me die?"

I shook my head.

She came right back at me. "Just throw me in the river."

I responded with a bit of lame humor. "Milly, I can't do that. It's cold outside, and all the rivers and lakes are frozen over."

She smiled and shook her head as if I should be ashamed of my lack of ingenuity. "Come on, Doc, that shouldn't stop ya. You're supposed to be a smart guy. Chop a hole in the darned ice and throw me in."

Looking on, her son, a Vietnam vet, displayed a lopsided grin and chuckled at his mom's persistence. The soldier knew his mom wanted to die, and he thought he was okay with it. She had lived a full life, and loneliness and pain were now her closest companions. Pete would never ask her to remain earthbound merely for his sake.

Her life had been tough going, and she was dreadfully tired. She was adamant that she would stay in her home of fifty years, and even when assisted living would've made far more sense, she insisted on remaining in her familiar dwelling. When death was closing in, she refused in-home care. "Pete can take care of me. He's a good son."

≥ ≥ ≥

WHILE HIS MOM LIVED, he held on. Soon she would be gone, and soon, very soon, he hoped he would be, too. And for the first time in a long time, Pete imagined an existence without torment: a day of termination would come at last, and he would smile a smile of relief. He wanted—he needed—to be a free man, to be released from these chains called "life."

An idle thought that had long ago wriggled its way into his brain now grew like a snowball rolling downhill, adding mass with each moment. The thought infected the soldier with a mantra of self-disgust. Over and over, a repeating commandment uttered words of condemnation: "you're worth nothing . . . you were afraid . . . you're worth nothing . . . you were afraid . . . you're worth nothing." On and on this message of revulsion tortured this soldier. This nemesis was not willing to rest; this parasite overtook his mind, infecting his thoughts with a primitive urge, morphing into a final command: "end it . . . you're worth nothing . . . you were afraid . . . end it . . . you're worth nothing . . . you were afraid . . . end it." His only solace was the familiar feel of the gun clasped in his hand. His gun would be his ally; he could count on it.

Before the winter ice had a chance to melt, Milly died, quietly and with dignity. And the soldier lost more than his mother. Pete lost the gift of distraction; no longer could he put off his evil pursuer. A demon stalked him without mercy and taunted him with hideous suggestions—mean-spirited chatter only he could hear—and this monster would settle for no further delay.

He broke. When his mom left, he could no longer hold off his torturer. His attacker would not rest, and Pete could not win. And so he would leave, too.

⁂

IT WAS AN AUTUMN DAY full of swirling leaves and warm sunshine when I entered the exam room and greeted Pete. I hadn't seen him since his mother had died several years earlier.

I remember feeling a horrid sense of "you've got to be kidding me" when he openly and unexpectedly disclosed that he had struggled with PTSD for forty years and recently had tried to commit suicide. He told me about his mental demons and that after his mom died he reviewed and settled his affairs. He oiled his gun and prepared himself to once and for all end his personal war.

Why did I not pick up on this inner conflict that was so powerfully hurtful for Pete? I have taken care of him for twenty-five years, and I never had a clue.

His story was astonishing, not for gruesome details on the battlefield but for the grisly trauma in his mind and the pain he had borne.

I asked him, "Pete, do you want to tell me what happened in Vietnam?"

"Yeah, Doc, I think I'd like to." And he did.

I HAD BEEN IN VIETNAM for about a year, and my responsibilities focused on the prisoner apprehension program. I traveled across the country delivering or picking up prisoners, getting them where they needed to be for various legal proceedings.

I never saw it coming. The mission was supposed to be routine, with three of us going to pick up two prisoners, both U.S. soldiers, and transporting them back to base camp. One of the prisoners was accused of killing another soldier in his platoon—which was weird—and the whole situation turned out to be anything but routine. So we picked up these two guys and were flying back to base on board a Huey helicopter when we were shot down very close to the Cambodian border. The pilot did a great job of landing the burning Huey, and none of us were seriously injured, so we were able to hit the ground running to get away from the flames as fast as possible. Everything changed when the helicopter exploded. The nearby trees caught fire and roared. We could just as well have put out a news bulletin that we were in the area, and sure enough, North Vietnamese soldiers realized an opportunity and rushed to grab it.

I figured hostiles would be spreading out, trying to outflank us, and things would heat up quickly. I wasn't wrong. Soon enough we could hear soldiers scurrying about the jungle, moving toward us, and though I didn't speak Vietnamese, I knew enough to know friends weren't on the way. I was nervous and scared thinking about being a POW in a North Vietnamese camp—a fate nobody wanted, for that was as bad as it could get.

We headed away from Cambodia, trying to find our way to a South Vietnamese base camp, moving as quietly and quickly as we could. I was so overwhelmed with fear I thought I'd throw up. I felt even worse watching my buddies: they seemed to be taking our situation in stride, and there I was, a scared sissy. I was disgusted with myself.

The next three days were hellacious, and we did our best to avoid engaging the enemy. Based on voices, sounds, and locations, we thought they probably outnumbered us by about ten to one. Doc, I gotta tell you: we were in a real pickle.

We desperately wanted to connect with friendlies—South Vietnamese or American soldiers—but we didn't know how. Our radios had been disabled when the helicopter blew up. We didn't know where to look. All we knew for sure was that enemy soldiers were tracking us and getting closer. Time wasn't on our side. We were in unknown territory and never knew what we would see on the other side of the next hill. We did everything we could to mask our movements and positions, but at night when things got quiet, so damn quiet, we could sometimes hear North Vietnamese soldiers talking and barking orders. They were close.

It was the third night out when things got really hairy. I was so terrified I could barely breathe. It was pitch black—no moon and no stars—and I was doing the final two-hour watch before dawn. I could occasionally hear rustling and mumbling coming from nearby jungle areas. Once in a while I would recognize some North Vietnamese words, so I figured enemy soldiers were moving in closer. We had taken cover on high ground under a rock outcropping and had hunkered down for about six hours. We lit no fires, and conversation was nothing more than a few whispered comments.

I wish I could forget that night, Doc, but I can't. My bowels felt like jelly, and my throat was so dry I couldn't swallow. I wanted to cry like a baby I was so darn panicky. My finger never left the trigger of the machine gun I cradled for two hours. I knew there were wetlands and a jungle to my left, and I could hear

North Vietnamese soldiers coming toward us from those areas. Their quiet chatter had the sound of strategizing. I hated myself for the fact that I wanted to call out and surrender. I wanted to live—I did not want to die in a battle I knew we couldn't win.

And just when surrender seemed like the best option, I would melt with fear at the thought of being a POW. And then I decided that I would rather fight and die than live as a prisoner. I vacillated between surrendering and dying for hours. I knew I was a coward, and I started to hate myself.

My watch shift seemed like an eternity, but finally scant rays of sunlight cracked the eastern sky, and my two buddies and I roused our prisoners and started moving to the east toward what we hoped was friendly South Vietnamese territory.

That morning I was point man, which meant that I did recon in front of the other guys. I saw movement about a hundred yards in front of me, and I jerked my rifle to my shoulder, sighting where the movement had been. I saw a soldier with a South Vietnamese insignia on his right shoulder, so I hollered at the top of my lungs, "Choo hoy!" which meant, "My friend!" The soldier turned and saw me and screamed likewise, and I fell to my knees and cried like a baby.

I had been so scared, and now that we had connected with friendlies, I could do nothing but weep. This made me feel even worse about being such a coward. My buddies had been so much braver than I. By the time they arrived at my position with the two prisoners in hand, the South Vietnamese soldier had already joined me with eight of his fellow troops. By then I had regained some composure, and we all marched out of the jungle together, arriving safely at a base camp in a few short hours.

"Pete, that's a powerful story. I have to confess, I had no idea what your Vietnam experience was like. That had to be absolutely terrifying."

"Doc, when I left Vietnam, I thought all the bad stuff was over and I would just get on with living my life. I was so wrong. Little did I know my toughest battle was yet to come. Soon after getting back home, I started experiencing odd thoughts—guilt trips, I guess—and they would not leave me alone.

My mind was like a combat zone, and something was always chasing me. I couldn't get away, and whenever I tried to hide by thinking of something other than Vietnam, these poisonous accusations found me and taunted me. Over time I realized the source of my torment was my gutlessness during that mission in Nam, and there was nothing I could do about it. I couldn't get away from the guilt. I was a mess and kept getting worse. I had a devil in my head, and I couldn't do anything about it. I hated myself. And yet there was Mom, needing me. I had to be there for her, but once she was gone, I figured the only way to gain any peace of mind was to just blow my brains out."

"I had no idea, Pete."

"How could you? I kept those thoughts locked tight in my head. Forty years after almost dying in Vietnam, my mom's death opened a door I had worked very hard at keeping shut. Her death gave me a funny kind of permission to go where I was afraid to go—a place I didn't want to visit but had to. I couldn't stay where I was with my demons. So something snapped. Did you notice you never saw me again after Mom died? I wanted to talk with you about my screwed-up thinking because I knew I was in trouble, but I couldn't do it."

Touching the back of his hand, I whispered, "Damn it, Pete, I wish I would have been there for you. I assumed you retired out West. I thought you had a cabin in Montana or somewhere like that."

"You couldn't have known. I was already pretty far down the road—miserable and confused and scared all over again, pretty much holding everything in until Mom left to meet her Maker."

"Pete, you were so good to your mom, always making sure her every need was taken care of. She may not have told you, but she told me many times how proud she was of you."

"Thanks. You know, Doc, I remember when she asked you to throw her in the river. I still chuckle about that every once in a while."

"She was a little stubborn," I said, "but her heart was always in the right place."

"Anyway, those days if I wasn't taking care of Mom, all I could think about was enemy soldiers wanting to kill me in the pitch black of night and me being a coward while my buddies were brave. Then Mom passed and the thoughts got worse and worse until they just took over. Looking back, I had already started to die. I just needed to pull the trigger, but when it got down to doing it, I couldn't."

"I'm sure glad you didn't, Pete."

"I was so messed up. And then one day—hallelujah, Doc!—one day a thought just hit me, out of the blue. It came into my mind to call the vets hospital, and I'm not exactly sure why I did it, but I did. I made the call. Those folks saved my life. I ended up spending a lot of time there. They told me I had a kind of nervous breakdown. A psychiatrist explained why I was feeling what I was feeling, and the counselors helped me look at bravery and courage in a different light. I was pretty mixed up, and it was really important for me to learn that fear isn't the same as being a coward. And sure enough, I slowly got better. I let go of a lot of poison inside my head and quit feeling so guilty, and now that I'm back, I'm here to stay."

I was probably so focused on his mom's illness and impending death that I didn't pick up on any hints or comments he might have made. I'm sure glad some good people were there to help him through his crisis.

Thankfully, Pete reached for help before pulling the trigger, and he was rescued from his tormentors. Talk therapy and pills did their job. Overcoming the pull of suicide, Pete had once again found value in living.

We talked a long time that morning. We discussed the fact that courage and bravery aren't simple concepts. Pete had learned at the hospital that **courage is not bravery without fear; courage is bravery with fear,** and this is what he had demonstrated in Vietnam. He and his buddies had refused to surrender despite incredible fear and trepidation. They all knew death could be avoided if they surrendered, but still, each one of these soldiers—individually—arrived at the same decision point. Life as a POW might be worse than death, and to volunteer for such a circumstance was an act none of them could commit. They were brave.

On the third night of a desperate trek in a land they didn't know and surrounded by enemy soldiers, Pete and his buddies confronted a dilemma of which few could dream. In the midst of hell, they elected to endure their fear because they chose to live any remaining days under the banner of freedom. They were courageous.

As G. K. Chesterton wrote, "he must desire life like water and yet drink death like wine." There and then, for one night, these soldiers held the power to turn water into wine.

෯ ෯ ෯

I THINK ABOUT PETE OFTEN, and I know he was far braver than he ever realized. His courage had shone brightly—in open warfare and private torment. In both situations he had been brave, and it took him forty years to realize it.

At his cabin amid a hellacious battle within the boundaries of his mind, Pete rejected the quicker solution—pulling the trigger. Courage preserved the gift of life, and today Pete is out and about—taking the dog for a walk, visiting with old friends, and sharing his lopsided smile everywhere he goes. He's getting better and stronger with each passing day.

The toughest battle this soldier ever fought was the biggest victory he ever won, and it took guts to prevail as his own gun was pointed at his head. Bravery is not deciding to be fearless; rather, it is accepting the risk of personal suffering. Pete was brave.

ఎ ఎ ఎ

PETE TAUGHT ME that PTSD is not simply a four-letter diagnosis having something to do with being anxious. It has more to do with shadowy places in the mind where demons dwell, holding the power to cannibalize their host. Even while he shared with me the story of three days in enemy territory in the middle of a miserable war, the telling took a toll on him. His eyes lost their luster, his face twisted from smile to grimace, and his cheeks hollowed with tension. Right there in front of me he was reliving his nightmares. **PTSD holds the power to destroy a life and can do so a hundred different ways.**

Pete carried his story quietly until the dammed-up emotions started to shake loose during the season of his mother's death. For more than forty years his nightmarish experience had remained bottled up, but this soldier got the help he needed—many soldiers don't. We can all take a cue from one who knocked on the door of death and somehow survived to see his life blossom again. By enduring his own personal hell, this hero bequeathed a lesson for doctors and patients alike: **the toughest battles can be fertile ground for the greatest growth—whether we like it or not.**

SAYING A LAST GOOD-BYE

"Doc, I know I'm dying. I don't think I'll be here next week."

Soberly I replied, "That's very possible, Roger."

Silence took over. Seconds stretched to minutes, and I sat quietly at his bedside, resting my fingertips on his forearm, feeling the enormity of his impending sojourn.

Roger interrupted my thoughts. "This dying business, it gets ya thinkin'. I guess I've always believed in some kind of heaven, but the more I think about it . . . it's not real clear, is it, Doc?"

I pondered his question. "No, it's not, Roger. From our side of things, heaven holds a lot of mystery, but there's probably a reason for that. We wait on this side of heaven's door, living a life filled with joy and pain; then we pass from here and learn a whole lot more about heaven and its goodness when we arrive on God's side of eternity."

"That makes sense, I guess, in a religious sort of way."

"It's hard to talk about heaven and dying without bringing a little religion into the mix."

I want to help him—maybe ease his mind a little. He's in awe of what's to come. Who wouldn't be?

"Roger, when I think about dying, I often reflect on a quote by C. S. Lewis: '**You don't have a soul; you are a soul. You have a body.**'"

"Ah, Doc—you better throw that one at me again."

"Lewis is saying we 'have' a body in the same way we might have a wart on our finger—it's temporary and really not that big a deal. We can't 'have' a soul, because a soul is who we are—it's our essence, the only part of us that has any enduring significance. What we can 'have' on earth is a body—full of atoms and molecules—but it's only temporary, just a short-term possession while on this planet. After ninety-two years, Roger, your body is pretty well used up: hard work and all the other demands of a century of living have taken their toll. The crippling arthritis and the worn-out joints and muscles, they don't matter anymore; it's your soul that counts—it's your soul that has worth, and your soul has no need for atoms and molecules. Soon enough you'll get rid of your physical body. Where you're going, you won't have any use for it. It has served you well, but you get to be done with it. And then you—your soul—gets to be free, really free, and your soul will experience that which it has waited for, for a lifetime."

He smiled slowly and murmured, "That's pretty heavy, Doc, but I think I get what you're saying. It makes sense. I've been thinking for some time that this old body is ready to give up the ghost. I guess it's just about time to be saying a last good-bye and praying for my soul."

I'm going to miss this man of honor. He's a World War II vet and a hardworking farmer who was still driving tractor last summer. He's a good man, and I don't think he needs to fear death one bit.

Roger had lived following the advice of Helen Keller: "use your eyes as if tomorrow you would be stricken blind; hear the music . . . as if you would be stricken deaf tomorrow." Yes, Roger had relished his time on earth and lived fully.

He may not see himself as an evangelist, but his life has sure been a testimony to the value of doing good things and being honest with self and others.

"Roger, I think you'll soon be on God's side of eternity, and whatever you encounter, it'll be good."

He smiled.

I patted his arm and said, "I'm going to be leaving now, but I'll stop by later. You're in my prayers. The nurses will keep a close eye on you. We'll make sure you're comfortable, and that's a promise. You let me know if there's anything I can do."

"Doc, I've known you a long time. You'll take care of me—thanks."

He closed his eyes, slumber bound.

Two days later, Roger died, uneventfully. His heartfelt reflections had been precious, and **it had been my privilege to be his private audience of one.**

🍂 🍂 🍂

WILLIAM AND I COULD pretty much enjoy discussing any topic—politics and religion for sure—and for more than a quarter of a century we had. Because he had been so very active in political arenas, he seldom missed a chance to express his views on current events. But a diagnosis of melanoma—a poisonous cancer insistent on attacking his brain and lymph nodes and anything in between—changed things. We spoke increasingly of issues surrounding dying, and he seemed more interested in listening than talking. Eighty years of living had done little to slow him down, but the dastardly melanoma was rapidly taking its toll.

"Doc, I've been thinking about this cancer. I know the score: this is an opponent I can't beat. The darned melanoma cells are probably spreading even as we speak. I think I'd like to die at home if possible. What do you think?" William asked.

"William, I think it's a good idea. You and your family are close-knit and see things similarly. I'll be glad to check on you at your house and make sure things are going okay. The focus would be pain control,

To be a blessing, words must resonate with the dying, be few in number, and presume not; otherwise they merely disquiet the soul.

dignity, abiding by your wishes, and addressing any family concerns. I've been involved in quite a few home deaths, and they can be a real blessing for both the patient and the family."

"Okay, Doc, why don't we sort of plan on that, and thanks for being willing to make some house calls if necessary."

"No problem, William, but please tell your family what you're thinking so everybody's on the same page. You don't want to have paramedics storming your house at midnight with lights flashing and sirens blaring because someone got spooked when you snorted or gasped in your sleep. **The traditional focus in medicine is aimed at extending life—not necessarily for the glory of living, but for the fear of dying.** You're asking that we suspend that approach and instead let you depart naturally from this earthly existence. Your attention has shifted to the next phase of your existence, and all the folks around you have to make that same adjustment. I think you're being practical, and I'll have no problem supporting you and your family in whatever way I'm needed."

It was quite a discussion, but it needed to happen if William was to get what he wanted—and what he wanted made sense. But it also required some planning.

᎘ ᎘ ᎘

"THE TIME OF MY DEPARTURE has come, I have fought the good fight, I have finished the race, I have kept the faith" (2 Timothy 4:6–7 ESV). These words I whispered slowly and carefully for William during a house call. His eyes smiled with a crinkling of his crow's-feet wrinkles. He understood.

"Amen, and thanks, Doc," he said ever so softly.

Time passed. His body weakened. Then it shriveled, and two months after our talk he surrendered to a relentless cancer. Encircled by a loving family, he quietly slid from this life to the next. Sounds of hymnal songs, rich in family tradition, echoed from the walls as he left his home to enter his Father's house with its many rooms.

A part of William's legacy that would carry forward resulted from his willing engagement with death as he chose to depart with grace and devoid of angst. He provided a lesson of ever-increasing pertinence in today's nervous climate regarding end-of-life issues. Exiting the familiar and comforting aspects of earthly life confuses and torments most souls. But William had made a profound and courageous decision when he refused to have his last months of life filled with appointments for more radiation, more chemotherapy, or more doctor visits.

He had finished the race, he had kept the faith, and he held in his heart the wisdom he knew: it is in dying that we are born to God's side of eternity.

I will long remember the slow and gentle nod of his head when I spoke my final words to him: "Oh death, where is your sting?" (1 Cor. 15:55 ESV).

William's last good-bye was a reflection of a deeply held faith that this life on earth is a dress rehearsal, and he was ready to move on. He chose how his last days would be navigated; his doctors did not. The insatiable appetite of the health care industry was denied a place at his deathbed. The opportunity to turn his last good-bye into an agonizing death march was given to no one.

≈ ≈ ≈

DEATHBED ENGAGEMENT is never easy and needs to be shaped by matching the spirit of the patient with the circumstances of the death. The aloneness involved in crossing the threshold from this world to the next should never be forgotten, and a caregiver is wise to remember that words are usually of secondary importance. Nevertheless, there are times when they may soothe a beleaguered spirit. **To be a blessing, words must resonate with the dying, be few in number, and presume not; otherwise they merely disquiet the soul.**

On the other hand, the gift of presence is a universal act of charity and may be the only offering the dying can perceive. **The touch of a human hand—far more than words—can express so profoundly the message, "Farewell and Godspeed on your journey."**

Sitting quietly with a departing soul can impart wisdom simply because two people shared awe-inspiring time together, one never to return and the other left to wonder.

Choices &
MIRACLES

A choice can birth a miracle,

a miracle can birth a choice,

and together,

they can deliver renewed life—

abundant and purposeful.

One Died—
One Lived

Two men, vital and active, suffered the same phenomenon—the network of cells stimulating the heart muscle failed, and each of them died. One required a eulogy; the other did not.

Brian had been alone when his heart faltered. He died, and I was asked to eulogize him.

For Gaylen, things played out differently. His wife heard his collapsing, lifeless body go *thump* against the bathroom door and went to his rescue. Her quick thinking led to a 9-1-1 call and the prompt initiation of CPR. The paramedics responded rapidly, and a speedy helicopter transport across town to a specialty hospital allowed a cardiology team to induce a lifesaving coma by cooling his body temperature to ninety-two degrees. For twenty-four hours, his body and mind lay inert in a chilling bed-bath. When the coma was slowly reversed with drugs and rewarming techniques, the result was a miraculous gift of new life. Within a day he was awake, and three days later he was sitting in his hospital bed chatting with his wife. His newly implanted pacemaker and internal cardiac defibrillator served him well. Gaylen's life had been saved, and no eulogy was required.

❧ ❧ ❧

THE PHONE CALL HIT ME HARD. It's always at least a little jarring to learn that one of your patients has died. But this call was intensely personal for me. When the coroner called and told me that my thirty-six-year-old patient and friend, Brian Revere, had died of a sudden and lethal rhythm disturbance of his heart, I couldn't believe it.

No, this cannot be! How can this happen? What about his wife? What will she do? And her kids—how will they manage? This just cannot be!

Brian was my age. We were contemporaries. We were dads. We were husbands. We were community volunteers. We were like so many other young men just starting out. We had the same dreams—pay the bills, save some money, raise good kids, be good fathers, and honor our wives. We strived to stand for God and country because we believed these things mattered.

And he's dead? I know his heart wasn't exactly normal. That's why I insisted he follow up routinely with the heart specialist. Brian assured me at our last visit that the cardiologist was satisfied with his rhythm and wanted to see him again in six months. This doesn't make sense.

I thought back to our visit when Brian had grudgingly consented to see the cardiologist. A couple weeks later he acknowledged it had been a good idea to do the heart workup. He was feeling better, and his heart was giving him no more bothersome palpitations.

But every time he saw me at the clinic, he would remind me, "Doc, I'm not afraid of dying. It will be the most natural thing I can do. I would like to stay around if that's what the Lord wants, so I can take care of Dee and the kids. But you have to quit worrying about me. I can see it in your face every time we talk. You had me see the specialist. I'm fine; you can relax."

Brian is gone now, his kids don't have a father, and Dee is alone. She's a single parent before she turns forty—how sad is that? How can I help her?

It didn't take long to find out the answer to my last question. In the midst of my struggle to digest this horrible news, the phone rang, and it was Dee, tearful and distraught. She asked if I would please deliver the eulogy for Brian's funeral service. Immediately I was pulled away from my own anguish and propelled into one of the more challenging roles yet encountered in my young medical career. I had to put aside my own remorse and help Dee and her family. I needed to postpone any of my own urges to grieve and instead do whatever I could for the loved ones Brian had left behind.

I have to come up with some words that will help the family. Their sadness has to be honored, and yet I must find a way to create hope that life will go on, and the future can still be full of love and meaning. This isn't going to be easy. How do I balance the sting of loss with Brian's strong conviction in a far better afterlife?

When Dee asked me to eulogize her husband, she gave me a chance to advocate one last time for a patient who had trusted me completely. As a man, he had earned my respect many times over, and as a friend, his death pierced me with the reality that we would no more connect and enjoy. I reflected long and hard. One thought, above all others, kept coming back to me—Brian's commitment to absolute candor. It made sense that this should be my focal point, and after much consternation, I decided to discuss a quote that had the ring of something Brian would say: **"Going to church does not make you a Christian any more than going to McDonald's makes you a hamburger."** This maxim displayed the teasing wit and frankness that were hallmarks of the way Brian communicated, and ultimately the mourners did express appreciation for a chance to consider the impact of his life from such a truism.

Brian's death served as a poignant reminder of how suddenly a person's time on earth could end. He was a good man who left us way too soon. We wanted him with us yet, but our want didn't change the unyielding reality: he was gone.

᳞ ᳞ ᳞

WHAT ABOUT MY OTHER PATIENT, Gaylen, a golf professional in his early fifties who died and lived again? How is it that he still walks the earth?

Near-death experiences (NDEs) have been rigorously studied, and scientific viewpoints are more opinion than fact. Deductive reasoning does not provide a blueprint for the actual truth. My own belief—influenced heavily by a career in medicine and devout personal convictions—is that miracles happen and NDEs can be miraculous. The powerful tools of logic and science have been unable to demonstrate any convincing reason for rejecting the miraculous nature of NDEs.

Based on forty years of study in chemistry, physics, anatomy, and theology, I believe miracles do happen. I perceive that many people who have "died" and then returned to earthly life with stories of an "attracting heavenly light" reveal insight from a prayer almost three millennia old: "I stand in awe of your deeds, Lord. Repeat them in our day. In our time, make them known" (Habakkuk 3:2).

Gaylen, the one whose life was renewed, stands as an "awesome deed" being made known in our time. He is alive, and his loved ones are not planning a funeral.

We shall be remembered by what we share with others.

Within this marvel there is an immense and challenging predicament for Gaylen, and he understands this. This gift of a mulligan, a death-defying do-over, commands both thankfulness and responsibility. When the time does arrive for his eulogy, how will he be remembered? **He will be remembered by what he shares with others, just as we, too, shall be remembered by what we share.**

Gaylen is a natural-born teacher, and his commitment to the art of golf instruction recaptured his energies soon after his near death. Teaching—the thing he loves to do—had to take a month off to give him time to die and live again. But his gift reemerged; it would not lie dormant. His passion for elevating the performance of his students demanded that his new life provide more opportunities to guide his pupils from the agonies of golf to the joys of improvement, giving hope to many that the next foolhardy eighteen holes might somehow satisfy.

Having survived an exploration of death, Gaylen returned with an understanding that what he gives to others will determine the content of his final tribute—yet to come, but come it will. He knows in an exquisitely real way that **tomorrow isn't his and never will be: today is the day he gets to use.**

The time for all eulogies will arrive. Brian is on God's side of eternity with his eulogy already delivered. Gaylen's eulogy waits. Two men, vital and active, suffered the same phenomenon but traveled different paths. Are their destinies linked? Who knows? Perhaps their worlds are a mere room apart:

> I have only slipped away into the next room.
> I am I, and you are you.
> Whatever we were to each other, that we are still.
>
> Call me by my old familiar name.
> Speak to me in the easy way which you always used.
>
> Laugh as we always laughed
> At the little jokes that we enjoyed together.
> Play, smile, think of me, pray for me.
>
> Let my name be ever the household word
> That it always was.
> Let it be spoken without the ghost of a
> Shadow upon it.
> Life means all that it ever meant.
> It is the same as it ever was.
> There is absolute and unbroken continuity.
>
> I am waiting for you, somewhere near.
> Just around the corner.
> All is well.
>
> Henry Scott Holland

Life is precarious and precious: seize it, love it, live it.

IF A CHOICE
SEEMS NOT YOUR OWN,
PERHAPS IT ISN'T

I left the church parking lot with a clear plan. It was a good plan—a couple hours of golf and then head home to read a book or take the dogs for a walk. I was tired. The previous week had been hectic and intense. Many critically ill patients—some of them too young to be so sick—had depleted my energy level. Trivial issues were beginning to irritate me—a good indicator that a day of rest was needed.

Face it, Scott, you're frazzled. You're taking some of your patients' problems personally and sleeping poorly. Today's the day to enjoy some quiet time. Your schedule for tomorrow is already full, so you know it'll be another busy week. Take a break. It'll be good for you.

After my little self-talk, I felt better. The need to finish monthly rounds at the nursing home had been nagging at me, but I could do that later in the week.

Good, it's settled: no medical stuff today, no nursing home rounds.

But there was some background noise going on inside my head that morning; my subconscious wasn't agreeing with my well-orchestrated strategy. An agitating notion kept pinging my brain, followed by my brain having an argument with itself.

Scott, you have only one patient to check on; see her today, and then you can eliminate that task from your to-do list. Why not go to the nursing home first?

Because I'm tired, and I've already decided—not today!

Don't you think you'd enjoy the golf more knowing your rounds were finished?

Good grief! Fine. All right . . . I'll go to the nursing home first, but I'm going to be quick about it!

I never did figure out why I gave in to the subconscious urge to delay the golf. Even more intriguing is the fact that my choice on that Sunday morning led to an encounter with Helmar Heckel, a man I had never met and would never forget. My life changed. A divine appointment? You decide.

≥ ≥ ≥

Choices are

not optional;

not choosing

is a choice.

TERRIFIC, *the elevator is waiting.*

I entered quickly and noticed that a well-dressed man near the control panel was the only other passenger. The doors closed, the cab rose, and a few moments later I quickly exited, needing only a couple of steps to enter the adjacent nursing station. Rapidly scanning the chart rack, I immediately realized my error and whirled around—the elevator doors were slowly closing. Two long strides granted me the opportunity to foolishly insert my left hand between the converging doors. Thankfully, the man inside pressed the OPEN DOORS button in the nick of time. My hand remained intact but my pride was not. Feeling a little sheepish about my hasty behavior, heedless of anything other than my own agenda, I murmured, "Thanks! Wrong floor—got out too soon."

He smiled graciously. "It happens."

The elevator creaked and once again slowly ascended toward my destination—the third floor.

"Are you a doctor?" he asked. (The stethoscope serving as my necklace must have been a pretty big clue.)

"Ah, yes, I am." An awkward silence ensued until my sense of sociability was reawakened, and I realized it was my turn to reciprocate with a question. "And you, sir, are you visiting someone?"

"In a manner of speaking. I'm here to visit anyone who wants to see me." He smiled at my perplexed expression. "I'm the chaplain, and our third-floor church service starts in a few minutes."

"Ah," I said, feeling no need for further discussion and having little interest in helping it evolve.

"Are you a Christian?" he asked.

What the heck? Did I hear him right? What kind of question is that? Granted, he saved my hand, but he hardly knows me well enough to be so personal.

"Well, yes, I am." There was silence, so I added, "It's a good thing what you're doing here. I mean, conducting the worship service. Thanks for doing that."

"You're welcome, but it's my privilege" was his response, and the doors opened to reveal the third-floor nursing station directly in front of us.

"Have a good day," I said, thinking those would be my last words to this engaging chaplain.

But as I took a step to leave the elevator, he reached out his hand and said, "My name is Helmar Heckel, and it was a pleasure to meet you."

"Oh, thank you, Helmar. My name is Scott Jensen. Maybe our paths will cross again. I have to finish my rounds now. Enjoy the day."

And with that, I proceeded to the chart rack and withdrew a brown, bulky, three-ring binder. I asked the nurse sitting at the desk if Gladys was in her room, and she nodded her head. I was back on track, and I could almost hear the golf course crooning, "Come to me, commune with nature, and practice to your heart's delight."

I did not find Gladys in her room, which was a little surprising. Rather, I discovered her sitting in the congregate living area, evidently waiting for Sunday worship to begin.

Fancy that, what a coincidence.

Anyway, I could be flexible, so I unobtrusively pulled her wheelchair into a private corner and quietly conversed with her. A brief exam followed, and I was pleased to conclude that Gladys was doing fine, with no new concerns. I concluded our visit and said good-bye. Wheeling her back to her front-row seat for the upcoming service, I turned to leave.

There stood Chaplain Helmar Heckel blocking my path.

"Ah, Dr. Jensen, could I possibly have a moment with you? Please."

"Well, sure," I said, wondering what was coming as Helmar guided me to a private alcove twenty feet away.

Over the next few minutes Helmar shared with me that the previous two days had been a most upsetting and topsy-turvy time for him. Forty-eight hours earlier during a routine colonoscopy, his doctor discovered a tumor in his large intestine, and the likelihood of colon cancer suddenly loomed on the horizon of his life. Helmar was candid and unreserved as he told me of his paralyzing fear and confusion. His story touched me in a special way, perhaps because both my parents had died from colon cancer.

Helmar was no ordinary chaplain. His gifts of sincerity and soft-spoken dignity were readily conveyed. His penetrating eye contact was unsettling, and the humble confession of his distress was gripping. I was accustomed to coaxing patients to share uncomfortable feelings and concerns, but Helmar simply laid the facts on the table without deception or hesitation. His request for assistance was simple and bold. His need was not hidden; its quality was raw and immediate.

"Will you help me, Dr. Jensen? I don't know what to do. I need someone I can trust, someone I can bounce things off of. I'm frightened."

His plea for help overflowed with earnestness and dread. The golf course didn't seem to be summoning me any longer; in fact, it was rapidly becoming a distant memory. "Yes, I'll help," I said. There were no second thoughts.

❧ ❧ ❧

I joined forces with Helmar. We exchanged phone numbers. He told me the names of the doctors involved up to that point. I was able to reassure him that his surgeon, a colleague of mine, was immensely talented. I researched facts for him; I called his surgeon to review the surgical plan; I analyzed his lab reports, and I told him what to expect. In short, I responded to Helmar's decision to trust me by advocating for him.

We became friends, and I included him in my prayers. He underwent major surgery, had a large portion of his colon removed, and recovered uneventfully. I followed up with him by phone to answer questions and encourage him through his trials. A month after we met, I received a letter from him. With his permission, I now share parts of it:

Dear Scott,

It was a month ago today that I met you in the elevator at the nursing home, going to the third floor. What you didn't know is that the very night before I had asked the Lord to send someone my way who could help me understand my situation.

After I learned that I had a large mass in my colon, the next 48 hours were filled with fears, questions, and confusion. Am I looking at the end of my life? That is when I cried out to the Lord, and He heard my cry and sent you. Listening to your words and learning a bit more about what I am facing settled me down.

I want to thank you for the wonderful comfort and truth I received from you. God used you to help me over a critical hurdle.

As it stands right now, the cancer was well differentiated, 21 lymph nodes were negative, and the oncologist recommended no chemo. Great news . . .

My wife refers to me as "the bird that escaped and is now free." Praise the Lord.

I would love to get together with you sometime and break bread.

Helmar, Campus Chaplain

Postscript: I need to spell out how lonely and desperate I was on that fateful evening after the discovery of the cancer. Too many words, ideas, and bad imaginations were bombarding my little existence. I was no match for what I was facing. It is amazing to me how quickly God answered me by sending you into that elevator that morning. The skill with which you approached me, the kinds of questions you asked, the expertise you had in that area, and the confidence you exuded all turned my face upward to my God. The day of threat and fear became a day of hope and promise. Thank you!

One day we met for lunch, and I shared with Helmar the weird set of circumstances that brought me to the elevator that Sunday morning. I spoke of my rush to get to the third floor in order to quickly see Gladys so I could retreat to my planned golf outing and enjoy a respite from medical matters. And I confessed that the time I spent with him gave my spirit more renewal than any golf session ever could.

≥ ≥ ≥

I HAVE LEARNED that an occasional day of separation from my never-ending world of medicine is good for me. The Sunday I met Helmar was supposed to be such a day. Happily, it didn't work out the way I intended.

C. S. Lewis said it well: "Every time you make a choice you are turning the central part of you, the part of you that chooses, into something a little different from what it was before."

Helmar's need called on me to readjust my schedule. A choice different from what I had planned behaved like a pebble tossed into a pond—the ripples went outward, effecting a cascade of actions and reactions too vast for any human to predict or measure.

Choices are not optional; not choosing is a choice. Helmar's insertion into my Sunday plans reminded me how a choice could have colossal ramifications. His choice to ask for help led to my choice to assist him. After he and I connected, he was newly energized. He asked, he learned, he analyzed, and he chose. Surgery was done. Healing occurred. And Helmar received the gift of newly invigorated life. He spread his wings and made more choices and "turned the central part of him into something new." And his "something new" touched other souls with compassion and empathy. I was privileged to play a part in this sequence of choices that informed an important chapter of his life.

I celebrate the memory of "Helmar and the elevator" often, and I am grateful that circumstances gave me the chance to make some choices I certainly had not intended.

≥ ≥ ≥

IF IT SEEMS A CHOICE is not your own, perhaps forces beyond your understanding are playing a role. This is a compelling lesson. In the church I attend, our pastor talks about "God promptings"—moments or events that may move us in surprising directions. The "whys and wherefores" of these occurrences are not usually apparent, but they are no less real. When unforeseen urgings cause me to make unlikely choices, I consider the possibility that Divine intervention may be altering my course. **To casually dismiss unanticipated happenings as coincidence may be an unfortunate error born of the human need to rationalize all that is not readily understood.**

Helmar reminded me of the gift of touching others. To more fully understand this, I needed Helmar to be my teacher, and he was. Helmar pushed through my crowded life and took a risk—he reached out and touched me. When I turned from Gladys, ready to scamper off to the golf course, there he stood, literally blocking my way. His interruption of my day was a touch no less powerful than if he had grabbed my hand and held it tight.

On a Sunday morning, I argued with myself until I finally changed my mind. I hopped on and off an elevator, giving rise to a conversation that otherwise would not have happened. On that day for whatever reason, Gladys chose to not rest in her room as she usually did. These facts led me to an unscheduled encounter with Helmar Heckel, who subsequently revitalized my will to serve others.

A coincidence? An answer to Helmar's prayer? A fulfillment of my unrecognized need? You decide.

A Fiend of
undeniable tenacity

This chapter is an allegory discussing the plight
of an actual patient, Connor, who is challenged
by the need to rigorously manage his heart disease.
Italics are used to describe a hidden world
where blood flows, vessels constrict,
and molecules run the show while a standard font
informs the reader of Connor's real-life predicaments.

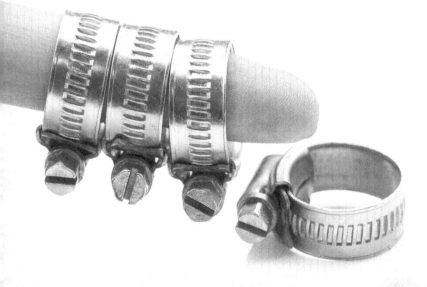

With no need for public appreciation of its efforts, the heart pumped and pushed, always doing its best to supply the tissues of its master with nourishing blood and oxygen. But something was amiss. Without the awareness of either master or itself, within its very walls, the heart had a betrayer on the scene—a villain plotting the master's death.

A scoundrel named Plaque roamed the maze of vessels embedded within the walls of the heart, cheering on the lethal marriage of fat and cholesterol molecules as they joined together to slowly block vital arteries with their own special concoction of sticky jelly. When total impasse was achieved, the mission would be accomplished—the master's river of life would come to a halt, the heart muscle would falter, and then, at last, the master would die.

The time was here, Plaque could see—a towering mound of fat and cholesterol almost completely choked off the passageway. Plaque added the finishing touch—a few more wedges of cholesterol jam—and the flow of life-sustaining blood came to a standstill. The vital vessel was stoppered like a cork in a wine bottle, and every downstream cell was instantly endangered. The maker of death sang its tune of demise.

❧ ❧ ❧

IT HIT! The pain hit hard. Connor knew something was wrong, but he could not be certain of what. Unfortunately, he did as fellow creatures have done for thousands of years; he misread the cause, assessing the aching pressure to be a problem of indigestion. The agony intensified, and while Connor delayed, the damage was done. The heart muscle was wounded, and Connor's life changed forever.

The gauntlet thrown down, the challenge was on. But Connor was no weakling, and his determination was legendary. This forty-nine-year-old man endured without complaint the intruding knife on his skin. His ribs were stretched to the breaking point. His heart muscle was tranquilized as a machine took over the work of pumping blood and oxygen to his organs and tissues. Three bypasses were crafted, and these virginal vessels gave rise to a restored river of life. Connor was made new!

Plaque was not pleased. Instead of delivering a fatal blow, its ominous toil had merely wounded the master, and now the weapon of surprise would be available no more.

Connor's heart attack was the wake-up he needed, and his keen mind developed a strategy for change. His determination did the work of rolling back the hands of time. He took pills and advice; he dieted and exercised; he changed and he flourished.

Meanwhile, Plaque wandered the labyrinth of tubes overlaying the heart of the master and searched for his old friends, cholesterol and fat. He found them strangely absent. Then he knew—yes, he knew—the master was fighting back. With a diet devoid of butter and pasta, the master had set about the task of denying Plaque's ill-behaved comrades the chance to permeate his blood. No more would his serum contain a never-ending supply of the ingredients Plaque required. Plaque was stymied.

≥ ≥ ≥

YEARS PASSED, and Connor had accomplished a monumental feat. His drive to prevail had done him well as he optimized his diet, dropped thirty pounds, reduced his cholesterol, lowered his blood pressure, and walked two miles a day without fail. He thrived while his invisible nemesis, Plaque, could do nothing but wait . . .

Unfortunately, human nature tends to pose questions that seek only to justify poor choices: Why am I committing myself to moderation as far as the pleasures of life? Is it really beneficial to reduce pasta and beer, or is Doc just messing with me? Isn't this daily exercise routine going to prematurely wear out my knees? Haven't I already done enough good things for my heart to last a lifetime?

Alas, for mere earthlings a compelling stimulus for change can lose its urgency as time marches on, and for Connor, his heart problem became a distant memory. He began to relax . . . too much.

The heart muscle continued its laborious efforts, pumping and pushing the life-sustaining oxygen-rich blood on behalf of its master. But something was wrong. It could tell its vigor was fading. Youthfulness had departed, and a lifetime of demands was taking a toll.

And then one day the devoted heart cringed; the old nemeses were back. Gone for a while, fat and cholesterol, Plaque's old buddies, were back, busy doing their dirty deeds again, invading and clogging. Plaque was a taskmaster, urging fat and cholesterol to never cease from their work of combining and congealing. Plaque thrilled to see the flow of the master's blood diminish to a trickle. Complete occlusion was in sight.

It hit! The pain hit hard. Connor knew something was wrong, and this time he recognized the problem in an instant. To the hospital he went, and without calamity two stents were inserted. Tests revealed that Connor's cholesterol was elevated, his weight had increased, and his blood pressure was not controlled. Ten years had passed since his long-ago crisis, and time had diminished his resolve. Connor had replaced salads and exercise with pasta and TV.

But once again Connor rolled up his sleeves and worked hard to change his unhealthy habits. With commitment renewed, he set about the task of losing weight and exercising. But something had changed. Youth and vigor were strangers as he neared his sixtieth birthday, and this time around his best efforts did not exhibit stunning results. The pounds didn't melt away. Exercise wasn't much fun, and cold weather hampered movement from the sofa. Nevertheless, his second cardiac event had been all too real, and the stents and added pills could not be denied. So he fought on and achieved the improvements he sought: weight, blood pressure, and cholesterol numbers all dropped; once again his will had triumphed.

৶৶ ৶৶ ৶৶

REGRETTABLY, after only a few years, his attention wandered and discipline dwindled: a small portion of lasagna would do no harm, a couple more beers might be relaxing, and the bread—goodness!—was so tasty one buttered slice would never be enough. Compromise for Connor became an invisible enemy wriggling its way into his reservoir of determination, imperceptibly increasing the risk that a day would come when no manner of change would do any good.

Plaque celebrated the human inclination for complacency. The master was falling asleep at the wheel, and Plaque would make him pay. Plaque lived for times like these, for he was a fiend of undeniable tenacity.

Connor had been threatened in his forties, but a bypass saved the day. In his fifties, two stents bought him time. Now in his sixties—would the mighty Connor finally strike out?

Plaque worked feverishly, engaging his comrades of old—fat and choles-terol—convincing them that strike three would be the moment of which they dreamt. Day and night, night and day, layer upon layer, sticky gelatinous chunks were meticulously positioned until the bloated Plaque nearly plugged the artery.

It hit! The pain hit, but not like before. It burned just a little, was easily denied.

"Damn heartburn!" Connor roared as he dug into his work. "I have no time for interruptions. There are deadlines to meet."

He continued his labors long into the night. He waited too long. Strike three was history.

When the doctors invaded and examined his heart, his principal vessel, the left anterior descending artery, was precariously plugged. Known as "the widow maker," its signature was death, and if this all-powerful obstruction could not be remedied, Connor was gone. But again good fortune served his heart muscle well, and the bullet carrying Connor's name was dodged. A lifesaving stent reopened this critical structure.

But this time the crafty villain named Plaque had planted seeds of itself in places not seen. While the heart was restored, the brain took a hit, and flecks of Plaque showered the master's language center, giving rise to a vocabulary of gobbledygook.

"Finally!" exclaimed Plaque with self-admiration galore. "The heart was my target, but choking off brain cells can be just as good. This time he is mine." Plaque was pleased.

Connor was afraid. He knew he spoke nonsense and couldn't find the right words. His heart had been salvaged, but this stroke business was new. He was weak in a strange way, and stenting the plugged brain artery was not an option. He drifted and dozed until consciousness was gone.

Only prayers remained, and eulogies were composed. Tears flooded the scene.

Yet again, somehow, someway, Connor was not done. While he wrestled with sleep, he saw something odd: from above he saw his own body—limp and pale as snow, with tubes of all sorts emerging and tangled—and this image never left him. He saw purring machines holding onto his life.

Now his grit came to bear, and once more he pushed back the angel of death as his legendary will did its work. He recovered yet again, but this third time—who knows?—could be his last. Willingly he took pills and advice; he dieted and exercised; he changed and flourished.

He lives, but the stakes have changed. Three strikes are up—does he dare to tempt another?

Heart health is a battle that all must wage.

☙ ☙ ☙

THREE TIMES their worlds had collided, Plaque's and Connor's. Yet somehow life had prevailed over death, and the fiend named Plaque was left dissatisfied while Connor's loved ones celebrated.

How does it end? That chapter's not written, but the poem of his life might be presumed:

> *Connor rallied, his life reborn.*
>
> *Plaque retreated only to sulk.*
>
> *Connor renewed, nothing to mourn;*
>
> *Plaque awoke ready to skulk.*
>
> *The battle goes on, who is to win?*
>
> *Plaque never quits, Connor will sin.*
>
> *Butter and fat again will appear,*
>
> *Betrayer aware his day draws near.*
>
> *What is the fate of Connor so frail?*
>
> *Does Plaque always win, man always fail?*
>
> *It's true we all do give up the ghost,*
>
> *Our bodies nothing more than a host.*
>
> *But when our defeat is all that remains,*
>
> *The Gift that's ours removes all our stains.*

≈ ≈ ≈

WITHIN CONNOR'S DILEMMA, a lesson emerges for all of us.

BUT WHAT ABOUT ME?

Do I harbor a fiend?

If it is to be,

Before I depart,

Before I must flee,

Should I, like Connor,

TEMPT A STRIKE THREE?

I Would Have
Prayed
for Death

In a moment Carla's life flipped upside down. And she knew it. Her mind frantically searched for an explanation. It was as if the electrical connections in her brain had suddenly gone haywire; her body was out of control.

She felt a commotion from within and realized she was falling. With no ability to regain balance, her body lurched forward and then spiraled clumsily to the floor. She heard the *thump* as she hit the floor. Momentarily stunned, she tried to sit up. Her extremities wouldn't move as they were supposed to, and her strength had abandoned her.

As she confronted a desperation she had never known, terror intensified her confusion. She needed help—and fast! This one thought was foremost in her mind as she fought to move. Getting on all fours was all she could do. Her effort felt pathetic. While crawling from the living room, she glanced over at the holiday tree and was surprised to see its dazzling lights twinkling with silvery prisms bursting from each bulb. She was crying.

She tried to assess what was happening and was horrified to feel saliva drooling from the right side of her mouth.

Despite her efforts to rush to the phone in her bedroom, each inch of progress took an eternity. Finally she reached up to her nightstand and blindly grasped for her precious lifeline. After punching it four times—three digits and "send"—she passed out. The noise of the emergency personnel breaking down the front door woke her.

The 9-1-1 call had its desired effect, and less than sixty minutes later Carla had been evaluated in an emergency room and transferred to a hospital specializing in stroke management. After an imaging test showed a large blood clot in a vital artery in the left side of her brain, she was taken to surgery in hopes of removing the devastating intruder. The noodle-like clot proved elusive and could not be extracted; its presence left a shattering imprint of chaos on the delicate network of nerve cells. Only a few hours earlier her brain had functioned like an efficient computer, but such a comparison would never be fitting again.

She had suffered a massive stroke, and this independent woman, accustomed to living alone and needing no one, would soon learn how difficult it could be to let someone help her with the simplest of daily chores. She would require months and maybe years in physical and occupational therapy programs to regain even a semblance of her former capabilities. She had to relearn the challenging demands of bowel and bladder management, eating and dressing, and rising and walking. If she was not successful, the local nursing home would likely become her permanent address.

In the aftermath of the stroke, it became apparent that not only had Carla suffered profound physical weakness on the right side of her body, but the language center in her brain had also been damaged. The result was an "expressive aphasia," which meant that her language skills were thoroughly disorganized, and she was ordained to stumble and bumble while attempting to express the simplest of thoughts. Carla was destined to learn that regaining the ability to speak and comprehend would be far more difficult at the age of sixty than when she had first acquired such skills in her toddler years.

With much stammering, shaking of the head, and scribbling on a pad of paper, Carla asked, "When can I do the things I used to?"

The neurologist's answer was "never," and unless a miracle took hold, this meant the rest of Carla's life would be a monumental struggle. Her daily life would focus on the simple and straightforward. Carla would have to outfox her brain by trailblazing new pathways around the tangle of dead nerve cells. She would find simple mental calculations such as four plus five exhausting and frustrating. Conveying even the simplest of desires would require mammoth effort.

The golden period for making progress in stroke situations similar to hers was generally twelve to eighteen months. She was in a race with the clock to recapture as much of her former self as quickly as possible, and Father Time was not her friend. She would fight her battle without the strength or coordination of the right half of her body. Her best efforts would be compromised by the reality that she could not look at a phone and say "phone," and if she wanted a fork, she was just as likely to ask for a spoon.

Sometimes life is just too hard. I don't see how Carla can do all that she needs to in order to really have a life. I'll be supportive—that's for sure—when I see her in the office, but I can't see anything good happening long term. What a miserable life she's in for. I wouldn't want it; it's just too much to bear.

Life has incredible worth, so never sell the human spirit short. What meets the eye is a shortsighted way to assess a life.

But bear the load she did. Displaying a determination her family did not anticipate, Carla gave witness to an inspiring inner strength. Though the stroke's initial wreckage left her so damaged that many of her friends wondered if it wouldn't have been better had she simply died, her resilience declared otherwise. Her courage was unending, and minor setbacks in therapy simply motivated her all the more.

I couldn't do it. I would have prayed for the touch of death. I never knew Carla was so tough.

Each passing month demonstrated the will and fortitude lying deep within her spirit. Carla proved everybody—especially the doctors and specialists—wrong. Whatever progress she might make was supposed to be completed within the first year or two following the stroke. But Carla did not stop at some arbitrary deadline. She would not give up. She gave testimony to human resolve. Her body continued its progress toward restoration. Regardless of how much had been taken from her, she expected of herself not merely a recovery but a new life, different from before, but meaningful nonetheless.

Two years after a crippling blood clot inactivated a section of her brain forever, Carla saw me for a follow-up visit. Her progress was stunning—nothing less than a miracle.

How is she doing it? She mows the lawn and then joins her friends for a glass of wine. She goes to soccer games to watch her nieces and nephews. She worships her God, singing His praises as never before. She humbles me.

Her life of healing continued. She met people. She encouraged people. She smiled with people, and wherever she went, Carla gave witness to the challenge that **regardless of what comes your way, you just have to make the best of it.** A debilitating stroke paved the way for Carla to give to others a gift that would keep on giving—a real-life testimony to the value of a resilient spirit.

≥ ≥ ≥

IN THE BOOK *Parochial and Plain Sermons,* John Henry Newman had this to say about the way our lives unfold and how devastating it might be to know in advance the results of our travels:

> Be not afraid. He is most gracious, and will bring you on by
> little and little. He does not show you whither He is leading
> you; you might be frightened did you see the whole prospect
> at once. Sufficient for the day is its own evil. Follow His plan;
> look not on anxiously.

≥ ≥ ≥

I SAW CARLA AND THOUGHT her life was over, that it was just a matter of time until she'd throw in the towel. I held the presumptuous view that I would have prayed for death. I didn't see value in her kind of living. I was wrong: Carla's life has incredible worth. She showed me that though a life without change or fear might seem to be an ideal objective, the ingredients of apprehension and unpredictability can combine with fresh challenges and accomplishments to create a new harmony; such rewarding music could not happen if death is embraced or opportunity denied. Carla's response to adversity revealed a transforming truth—**whether in the throes of paralyzing consternation or the joys of triumphant dance, life can and should be lived fully and passionately. I sold her short, and in so doing, I sold the human spirit short—shame on me.**

As for Carla's current whereabouts, she's probably out and about, meeting a friend for coffee or lifting spirits. For certain she's living the message: **what meets the eye is a shortsighted way to assess a life.**

"BE NOT AFRAID.

HE IS MOST GRACIOUS,

AND WILL BRING YOU ON

BY LITTLE AND LITTLE."

DON'T LOOK BACK

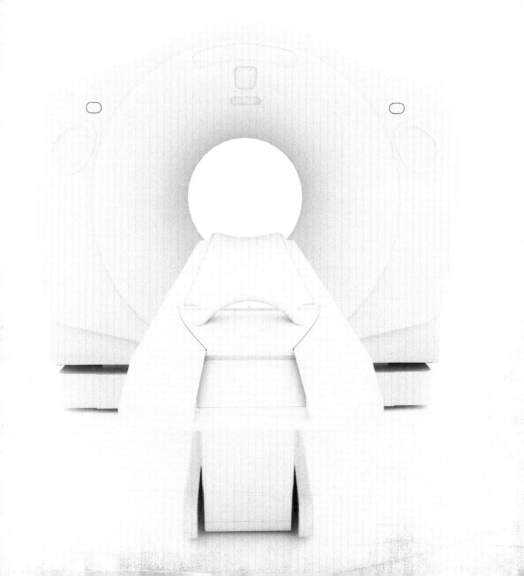

My eyes automatically went into squint mode, as if this would allow more information to be gleaned from the CAT scan in front of me, but no amount of additional scrutiny would make a difference. I had already reviewed the scan three times and knew one of my dearest patients was in trouble.

A nurse walked by the brightly lit view box and stopped. "What's that big white spot?"

"It's a pool of blood in the right side of Linda's brain. When she was in Japan two months ago, she had a stroke, and unfortunately it was a big one. This walnut-sized white area is blood that collected in the area where her artery broke, and it's so darned big, it's a miracle she's alive. Her future is uncertain: at times the body can heal something like this, but usually not. I told her this morning we'd just have to see what happens; there's really nothing we can do other than watch and wait."

"Gee, Linda is such a precious soul—always friendly and interested in others. I hope she does okay," the nurse replied.

"I couldn't agree more—she is a delight. When I told her that it's too soon to know how everything will turn out, she simply smiled and told me she was moving forward and not looking back. Then she reminded me that God is in charge of her destiny."

The morning had been emotionally draining, and my lunch break was spent quietly thinking about Linda. I reflected on the story she had told me a quarter of a century ago.

ɪ ɪ ɪ

ON A FATEFUL THURSDAY, the ninth of August 1945, Linda's remarkable account began. She had just turned thirteen, and even though the Allied forces had achieved victory in Europe, World War II continued in the Pacific arena.

On that summer morning, a few moments before eleven o'clock, Linda and her ten-year-old sister, Miyako, were chatting and laughing with friends on a fun-filled playground. They were unaware that a high-flying bomber plane had just released a deadly cargo into an azure sky, clear and calm. A few minutes later an atom bomb nicknamed "Fat Man" detonated 1,500 feet above the streets of Nagasaki.

Suddenly Linda's universe was lit up by a flash so brilliant it was as if the sun had emitted a last gasp of energy to burn brightly for one single final moment. The dazzling splash of light was followed by an earsplitting thunderclap, and the ground shook. "Fat Man" emitted a heat so intense a swirling monster was born as temperatures at the blast site exceeded five thousand degrees. An unholy wind, sizzling hot and deafening, exploded onto the scene with speeds exceeding five hundred miles per hour (greater than the strongest of hurricanes). Its killing force was butchery as it pitched anything and everything from its path, and some of Linda's schoolmates died horribly when their airborne bodies were pulverized against nearby buildings.

But on this day Providence reached out a protective hand, and Linda and her sister were shielded from death. The hot tsunami wave knocked them backward, and they stumbled, falling fortuitously into a crevice created by an earthen depression and an adjoining low concrete wall. They lay gasping and stunned, viewing a reel of images never to be forgotten. Seeing their friends tossed about, twisting and turning like a macabre puppet show, they could not imagine what was yet to come.

From her vantage point, Linda glimpsed a young mother on a nearby sidewalk struggling to hold onto the hands of two children. She stared mesmerized as the woman leaned mightily into the furious wind, looking around for some kind of help or shelter, when the hurricane-like gale suddenly gusted and violently tore into this family. The force was hellacious and deadly and instantly the necks of the mother and her two kids gave way and twisted beyond human limits. Linda's eyes glistened as she described the ghoulish image of three contorted heads sagging on lifeless shoulders as their bodies staggered forward in a grisly dance of death before collapsing to the ground.

Seeing the light, hearing the explosion, feeling the heat, and watching the calamitous force of the wind—these inputs informed Linda her life would never be the same, not ever. There was no way for her to realize then that she stood only one mile from ground zero of the most powerful weapon ever unleashed on planet earth, and that her survival was an absolute miracle.

From the center of the city an ominous cloud took shape and loomed as a sacrificial spire. Linda's voice quavered when she described the image of a massive mushroom haze rising to the heavens with a fat gray stalk trailing to the ground. Ugly and terrifying, it shadowed the land and lingered for days. The sun shone not and a deadened twilight bathed the living.

"The cloud didn't go away in a few hours," she told me. "It wouldn't go away even after a couple of days. It stayed right where it was, not moving, fouling our spirits and cursing our people."

Linda and her sister left the refuge of the school, which had become a makeshift cemetery with twisted bodies of former playmates haphazardly on display, and headed homeward. Sidewalks were so hot that rubber-soled shoes melted and stuck to the cement like glue. Everywhere Linda looked, she saw the devastation of this not-to-be-believed maelstrom as the two girls picked their way, avoiding the uprooted trees filling the streets and the cars littering the walkways.

"I saw clumps of my hair fall to the ground, and my clothes were so scorched I could peel them off my body like paper," Linda shared in a whispery voice raw with emotion.

The two-mile hike home was nothing other than a death march. Their path was littered with friends and neighbors—bleeding and broken, begging for solace.

"We had to fight our way home through the debris and bodies. People would reach out and grab my leg and beg for water. People were lying everywhere, crying for help, crying for water. '*Mizu, mizu* [water, water],' they were screaming, their faces tormented with pain. Some had intestines hanging out of their bellies. It was a horrible sight." Linda and her sister could offer no help.

The miracle of their survival—the magnitude of its impossibility—was slowly revealed.

"How we survived, I don't know," Linda said.

The girls were finally united with their mother at a bomb shelter after miles of walking and hours of tears. Even their mother's arms could not shield them from the stink of death or the sounds of dying.

"Sometimes there were noises in the night like someone was popping popcorn. I learned it was a sound from the dead—their stomachs were popping—and I was sickened. And the bodies smelled so terrible, but there was no one to remove them. The dead were everywhere."

Linda and her sister experienced firsthand the powerful purging effects of poisoned water, and days of vomiting and diarrhea left both children with lasting memories of why they should have listened to their mother's warning to drink only "safe" water.

Amidst these horrors, Linda had not yet learned of one final price to be paid: the bomb had rained down invisible radioactive fallout, soaking thousands with a toxic contaminant willing to wait a lifetime before revealing its mutilating effects.

⁄◦ ⁄◦ ⁄◦

BUT LINDA LIVED. During a clinic visit she confessed, "I believe God meant for my sister and me to survive. I call this my second life. But because we lived and many of my friends died, I still feel guilty."

Somehow, not only did she live, she healed. Many years later she met an American GI based in Japan, and they fell in love. They married. When his term of duty was over, they moved to Watertown, Minnesota, and raised two wonderful boys. In her new home, Linda was tireless as she managed the obligations arising from the need to wear many hats—wife, mom, friend, and business owner.

It was her cozy little restaurant that brought us together. We connected because I called her café and ordered a take-out lunch. A few weeks later she came to see me as a new patient, and so started a relationship that continued for more than twenty-five years.

Sadly, her final trip to Japan to visit family had brought new disaster. The massive cerebral hemorrhage had almost killed her. She was very ill and remained in the hospital for weeks. But she lived and was able to return to her home in Watertown, ready to rehabilitate and display once again her gift for survival.

⁄◦ ⁄◦ ⁄◦

SHORTLY AFTER RETURNING HOME, Linda came to see me in the office for a follow-up visit. I reviewed the CAT scans she brought with her, and there was the pool of blood my nurse asked about. It was an ominous blob obscuring a large part of her brain. According to Linda, the doctors in Japan had been pessimistic about her potential for recovery, sharing a prognosis of substantial disability for an eighty-year-old woman. The sheer size of the stroke allowed no other conclusion.

But Linda defied their predictions: she thrived.

She saw me a month after her therapy program had begun, and she was stronger. She saw me six months later, after her therapy sessions had ended, and she was stronger still, her thinking processes sharp and alert. A year later, she was virtually back to normal. I was astonished. Incredibly, a follow-up CAT scan revealed no pool of blood—not even a shadow of the original damage. All evidence of her stroke had disappeared. It was my joy to share the remarkable news.

"Linda, you are a walking miracle: the pool of blood in your brain has completely disappeared. You have no residual weakness. You are amazing."

"Oh, not really, Dr. Jensen. I'm a pretty ordinary person, just like everybody else." A playful grin creased her countenance, but her eyes shimmered with tears of gratitude as she assimilated the news that her brain had healed.

The story of Linda Seck (known in Japan as Yukio Schimada) has been for me a wellspring of inspiration and wisdom for nearly half my life. When Linda declared herself to be an ordinary person, I was reminded of a comment by C. S. Lewis: "There are no ordinary people. You have never talked to a mere mortal. It is immortals whom we joke with, work with, marry, snub, and exploit."

*Linda is no ordinary person—that's for sure—and truly **there are no ordinary people. We all have a story.***

⁂ ⁂ ⁂

I WILL NEVER FORGET the day Linda lectured me on logic and truth. We were discussing World War II and Japan and the United States. This was not our first such foray into heavy-duty political sharing.

"Remember, Dr. Jensen, bombs don't cause wars; people do. Bombs kill and destroy because people would have them do so. It is people who choose to use them. Remove the bombs and you haven't really changed anything. Other weapons will replace them. Mankind has already traveled from sticks and stones to slingshots and spears, from bullets and bombs to anthrax and the Twin Towers—people make choices."

Her words brought to mind a story I had read by G. K. Chesterton:

> The wind tugs at the trees as if it might pluck them root and all out of the earth like tufts of grass. The trees are straining and tearing and lashing . . . I remember a little boy who was walking under just such torn skies and tossing trees. He did not like the wind at all; it blew in his face too much; it made him shut his eyes; and it blew off his hat. He was, as far as I remember, about four. After complaining repeatedly of the atmospheric unrest, he said at last to his mother, "Well, why don't you take away the trees, and then it wouldn't wind." Anyone looking for the first time at the trees might fancy that they were indeed vast and titanic fans, which by their mere waving agitated the air around them for miles. Nothing could be more excusable than the belief that it is the trees which make the wind.

Linda understood that eliminating bombs would no more prevent war than removing trees would stop the wind. She knew that people caused wars, and bombs were nothing more than an effect, like a prop in a play. She had delivered a simple and logical lesson to her doctor. **It is dangerous to confuse cause and effect; fanning trees don't cause wind, and bombs don't cause wars. Own the courage to see the truth.**

≈ ≈ ≈

LINDA WAS EVER A TEACHER. Her lasting instruction for me was this: **Look forward; don't look back.** Despite all that had happened to her, she had found strength through pressing on, believing in the goodness of tomorrow, avoiding the tragedy of backward viewing. She inspired a poem.

A warm and sun-filled summer morn,
playground squeals and laughter.
Few burdens were there to be borne,
a life of happiness ever after.

Above, a bomb began a race,
to strike and wound our inner core.
A war had risen, shown its face,
sund'ring hearts forevermore.

Now a mirror from which to learn,
sees through ashes recent gone,
views a chance for love's return,
beholds the gift—a brand-new dawn.

When the poem was completed, I realized another miracle of Linda: hers was a heart never sundered—not for a day and not forevermore. For Linda Seck/Yukio Schimada, there really was no looking back; it was all about a brand-new dawn and the promise of the day to come.

❧ ❧ ❧

THEN ONE DAY she unexpectedly came to say good-bye. She and her husband were relocating to a warmer clime, closer to their son. I would sorely miss her—her joy-filled spirit, her eager encouragement, and her absolute conviction to always move forward.

It's hard to believe I won't see Linda's name on my schedule again. Her absence will be my loss.

She had survived an atom bomb, radiation poisoning, and a pool of blood in her brain. She was a walking miracle, and now was walking out of my life. Saying good-bye to her was one of the most difficult things doctoring had asked me to do. The lump in my throat, the tears in my eyes, the prayer in my heart—they were my wordless farewell.

As the door closed behind her, the wisp of a touch stirred my conscience—had I heard the words, or had my meditations given them birth? Somehow I came to understand a final command: **"Don't look back. The answer lies in the opposite direction."**

EPILOGUE

FOUR THOUSAND YEARS of recorded history reveal a long and rich tradition of patients and healers working together to determine "cares needed" and "services provided," but the last fifty years gave birth to an extraordinary phenomenon as government agencies and big business made a dramatic entry into the personal realm of serving the sick, fixing the wounded, and consoling the dying.

Recently this invasion of private lives has shown impressive momentum, with consequences so far-reaching that patients and doctors must respond or else resign themselves to a fate filled with frustration. What began in the 1950s as an optional common-sense insurance initiative with patients retaining the majority of responsibility for health care bills has morphed into a massive involvement of mega stakeholders competing for market share and influence. These entities have demonstrated a relentless appetite for control and power, and at the same time the once-sacred relationship between patient and physician has been devalued and is in danger of becoming a relic of the past, more like a Norman Rockwell painting than a vital bond tethered by a patient's trust and a doctor's advocacy.

In today's medical world the patient has become a pawn and the physician resembles a technician. A corporate mentality has insinuated an agenda having little to do with trust or empathy, hallmarks of the Hippocratic Oath. Untraceable decisions to reduce services or increase premiums cause patients to be wary and frustrated. Seldom does a day go by without my patients expressing concern about a denial of coverage for lab tests, MRIs, mammograms, vaccines, or medicines. Questions arise: "What services will be eliminated next? Why aren't these pills covered? What if I think I need a test and my insurance company says no? Do my beliefs matter at all?"

Today the patient stands in harm's way— alone— because his voice has been weakened.

Thirty years in the trenches has convinced me that patients want to be in charge of their health matters and should be in charge of their health matters. Patients understand and embrace the concept that one size doesn't fit all. Some seek to prolong life at any cost, while others accept an abbreviated time on earth in order to remain free of outside interference. There is no one right answer, but perhaps the only wrong answer is to have Big Brother steal that which is not his to take.

To make matters even more difficult for the modern-day patient, our health care system has become saturated with a jargon requiring comprehension of terms such as *prior authorization, maximum benefit, high deductibles, standard of care, prescription gaps, non-formulary drugs, donut holes,* and *lifetime expenditures.* Without a grasp of this medical lingo, a patient seeking help for a cough, nosebleed, or laceration does so at some peril—financial and otherwise.

It's time to reexamine how we tend to the needs of the sick and the dying. Assembly-line care and patient quotas may intersect nicely with the growing influence of the computer screen, but the connection between the receiver and the provider of medical care is the victim. Never before has caring for the suffering involved so little of what it is to be human.

This is a trying time to be a patient or a doctor. Our system of care is driven by bureaucrats, and physicians are funneled toward productivity measurements by organizations that no longer embrace the concept of doctoring as a calling. A "mass production" approach to caring for people encourages an environment wherein doctors might view their next patient,not as someone in need of help, but instead as an obstacle to staying on time or a hindrance to meeting quota expectations. This vexing set of circumstances forces patients to navigate—unsupported and alone—the minefield of risky interventions ordered by doctors who are too often in a hurry, disillusioned, and burnt-out.

This book addresses the power of relationships. It celebrates the bond between the receiver and giver of medical care and calls for this bond to endure all seasons and serve as a light of renewal for our system of caring. Relationships matter now more than ever, and patients and doctors both derive needed hope from trust and advocacy.

ه ه ه

Dr. Paul Brand was a pioneering physician who devoted his medical career to the study of pain and the relief of leprosy victims. He told the story of an old man with leprosy who would reach into a bed of hot coals with his bare hands to turn a roasting potato. Dr. Brand used that observation to discover that the disfigurement that makes leprosy such a dreaded and hideous disease stems from the fact that a person with leprosy cannot feel pain. The old man no longer treated his fingers as something worthwhile or part of himself because his fingers felt no pain. Dr. Brand elaborated that a healthy body attends to the pain of its most vulnerable part.

His conclusions established a basis for treating leprosy, but they also portray the essential wrong in our current system of medical care. "Attending to its most vulnerable part" should be a characteristic of any health care organization, but this is not the case with twenty-first-century medicine.

Today the patient stands in harm's way—**alone**—because his voice has been weakened, and his traditional advocate can no longer be assumed to be at his side. How could this happen?

This is how it could happen: While amazing science fiction ideas of yesterday became routine tools for today's doctors, long-held appreciation of the bond linking those who suffer with those who heal faded. Science trumped caring. Technology replaced empathy. Dollars dissolved dedication. Patients lost trust. Doctors forgot advocacy. And here we are.

What can be done?

Patients and doctors must mutually reaffirm the vital nature of their bond. Together they must build and maintain compassionate relationships infused with trust and advocacy so that the need of the patient is tethered to the service of the physician.

The foundation of medical care is fracturing, and relationship matters.

Alone, there is so much we cannot do; together, there is so little we cannot do. Together, we can remedy the damage to our precious bond and once again cherish the gifts we bring to one another. The time to act is now.

Chapter Summaries

"Doc, Can You Save Her?"

Today's world of assembly-line health care is driven by an appetite for profit and power and doesn't pay much attention to relationship-building. The corporate neutering of a meaningful patient-doctor relationship can occur dramatically and without warning.

Crisis at 37,000 Feet

The touch of death heightens our awareness that life is a fragile gift and that humans touch one another in inconceivable ways. Within the mysterious walk of everyday life, we are all confronted with startling opportunities to see grace in action.

The Prescription That Should Not Have Been

Medical decision-making in the new millennium must include patients as fully participative partners working with doctors in the process of planning and carrying out interventions. Doctors can walk away from the adverse impacts of pills they prescribe or the interventions they plan; patients may not.

"That's What I've Been Trying to Tell You!"

Listen to comprehend; don't just hear words or go through the routine. Ask real questions and wait for the answers. Never forget: it's all about understanding. Assumptions lead to misdiagnosis.

"Until I Die, Honor My Wishes"

In this day and age, patients need to be far more than passive followers regarding life-and-death issues. They deserve the chance to direct their care, and assertiveness may be necessary. In life and death, the patient's wishes should be honored.

"Doctor, Are You Happy with Your Job?"

Patients and physicians need one another. They support one another. The value of a physician's service to a patient is usually plain to see, but the reciprocal gift from a patient—a renewing force that sustains a physician's commitment to healing—is easily overlooked.

Embrace the Attitude; Gain the Latitude

If we can embrace another person's attitude, we are given the latitude to go where we might otherwise not be welcome. Embrace the attitude, gain the latitude, and a powerful bond may grow.

"It Is in Giving That We Receive"

Patients should never forget this: doctors need you, in ways you cannot know, in ways you could not guess. Physicians should remember that there is art to medicine as well as science, and that warmth, sympathy, and understanding may outweigh the surgeon's knife or the chemist's drug.

A Snake with Pneumonia

The value of developing strong working relationships with your staff cannot be overstated. Leaning into their knowledge and experience helps you develop the skills and know-how you need to become proficient in your role.

Patients Can Be so Precious

The magical enchantment humans hold for one another and the intriguing chemistry our Creator instilled into men and women are certainly not age dependent.

The Unexpected Double Whammy

"Expect the unexpected," because surprises are the norm in the world of emergency medicine. Do-overs are luxuries not often granted, and we live with unfavorable consequences. Learn that lingering self-incrimination serves a valuable purpose by etching forever in your mind those occasions of flawed judgment.

Patients Share the Blame

The "want" of a patient is not equivalent to the "need" of a patient, and when the "want" serves as the sole driver for ordering tests and other interventions, avoidable and disastrous outcomes will occur—it's just a matter of time. Interventions that appear safe and well-intended can still be lethal and unnecessary. When it's decision-making time, the difference between a "want" and a "need" must be carefully considered.

Offering a Different Perspective

A physician's perspective doesn't become the patient's perspective merely because of words. Persuasive teaching efforts devoid of any sense of bullying combined with genuine compassion go a long way toward convincing a patient to get on board with the doctor's recommendation.

When Two Sounds Are Better than One

In today's world of electronic medical records, patient care can be immensely improved by the simple act of a physician picking up the phone and speaking directly with a colleague about the patient's status. Never lose sight of the value of direct communication, even if it takes more time and effort.

Be Careful What You Ask For

Medicine is not all cures and transplants; interventions are imbued with risk, and it is the shrewd patient who takes seriously the responsibility of saying yes or no to recommendations for tests or procedures. Candid—often awkward—discussions may be the only way to avoid unnecessary interventions.

Avoid Dead Carpenters in the Living Room

Be willing to consider the possibility that a Divine prompting is sparking the notion to make a call or take an action out of the ordinary. Casually attributing strange events to mere coincidence may deny you the chance to see the miracles in everyday life, and that would be a pity.

The Last Thing Dad Taught Me

Preoccupation with your own feelings will hinder your ability to see another's pain and fear. Remember that it will always be too soon for a loved one to leave this earth from your point of view. Consider Bob Marley's wisdom: "The truth is that everyone's gonna hurt you—you just have to find the ones worth suffering for."

A Doctor in the Making—a Work Never Finished

The suffering patient serves as a never-ending source of instruction from which doctors continue the ongoing process of learning and growing as they "practice medicine." Life is fragile and uncertain—there can be no taking it for granted.

Suicide Victims Teach from the Grave

Grief arising from suicidal death is not reconciled by trying to solve the mystery of *why* the victim chose an early exit from life. Celebrate the pieces of the victim's life that allow for rejoicing and embrace these memories often. Compassion extended to others has an odd way of coming full circle, helping to heal even the most obstinate of wounds, especially the ones that keep welling up to capture our heart all over again with an unpredictable wondering about the *whys* and *hows*.

She Deserved Better

When doctors are faced with not knowing the answer to a patient's problem, they may abandon the art of medicine and carelessly use words to cast blame anywhere but on their own shortcomings. Don't be too willing to accept as gospel truth all that the doctor claims.

The Pain of Inadequacy

There are no answers to some of life's issues, and we need to admit that. But a simple trust in something beyond the human realm can reveal a way for our souls to make peace with the challenging words "I don't know."

Grief Unresolved

Grief can become an indomitable, relentless force. No one can avoid grief, but it can be rendered less crippling by confronting it. The balm for a grieving wound contains three ingredients: be involved with the grief of others, expect grief to show its face often, and accept grief as an inescapable part of life.

Face of Aging—Gratitude and Grace

It makes no sense to get in a tug-of-war with a chronic disease or growing old. Learn to say, "it is what it is," and try to chuckle, at least a little. Learn how to be grateful when things are good and how to be graceful when things are not so good.

He Did It His Way

Mourning is a powerful catalyst for transformation. Past transgressions, emotional scars, and lasting resentments—all sorts of painful memories—get scrubbed clean, and then "letting go" can happen, opening the door for the gift of renewal to work its magic.

Too Much Sanity May Be Madness

Conversations regarding emotional or mental health concerns do not lend themselves to quick and easy explanations. There is simply no substitute for a heart-to-heart discussion before any prescriptions are written. Positively affirm the person's uniqueness and expose the idea of anyone truly being "normal" as an impossibility.

"Doc, I'm Not Happy with What's Going On!"

Patients need to be in charge of their own health, and doctors need to be patient advocates. Our health care system will be the loser if patients' voices are not heard. Patients and physicians, working together, make a formidable team, and both benefit from mutual trust and advocacy.

A Soldier's Toughest Battle

PTSD holds the power to destroy a life and can do so a hundred different ways. Courage is not bravery without fear; courage is bravery with fear. The toughest battles can be fertile ground for the greatest growth—whether we like it or not.

Saying a Last Good-bye

To be a blessing, words must resonate with the dying, be few in number, and presume not; otherwise they merely disquiet the soul. The gift of presence is a universal act of charity and may be the only offering the dying can perceive. The touch of a human hand—far more than words—can express so profoundly the message, "Farewell and Godspeed on your journey."

One Died—One Lived

Tomorrow does not belong to us and never will: today is the day we get to use. We shall be remembered by what we share with others. Life is precarious and precious: seize it, love it, live it.

If a Choice Seems Not Your Own, Perhaps It Isn't

To casually dismiss unanticipated happenings as coincidence may be an unfortunate error born of the human need to rationalize all that is not readily understood. If it seems a choice is not your own, perhaps forces beyond your understanding are playing a role. Consider the possibility that Divine intervention may be altering your course.

A Fiend of Undeniable Tenacity

Heart health is a battle that all must wage. The great fiend Plaque silently roams the maze of vessels embedded in the walls of the heart, commanding fat and cholesterol to slowly block vital arteries and cause death. Diet and exercise and determination stymie Plaque's efforts. Will we resist his mission to seek and destroy?

I Would Have Prayed for Death

Sometimes life can seem just too hard. Regardless of what comes your way, you have to make the best of it. Life has incredible worth, so never sell the human spirit short. What meets the eye is a shortsighted way to assess a life.

Don't Look Back

There are no ordinary people in this world. Everyone has a story—a unique story. No matter what happens to us, we must find the strength to press on and believe in the goodness of tomorrow. We must not look back—the answer lies in the opposite direction.